Sto

D1327190

MASTER DETECTIVE

ALLAN PINKERTON

BORN: August 25, 1819

DIED: July 1, 1884

In 1842 Allan Pinkerton was forced to flee his native Scotland to avoid political persecution. He settled in Illinois, became a detective by accident when he exposed a ring of counterfeiters and soon was hired by the Chicago police. His high standards and sound methods of police work produced such amazing results that he set up his own agency. In 1860 he uncovered a plot to assassinate Lincoln, and his swift action saved the President's life. Then during the Civil War he established, at Lincoln's request, the first United States Secret Service bureau where he directed all espionage and intelligence work for the North. From his stirring exploits emerges the portrait of a man who served the cause of justice with rare dignity and principle throughout an illustrious career.

MASTER DETECTIVE
ALLAN PINKERTON

by
Arthur Orrmont

JULIAN MESSNER, INC.
NEW YORK

Published by Julian Messner, Inc.
8 West 40th Street, New York 18

© Copyright 1965 by Arthur Orrmont

Printed in the United States of America

Library of Congress Catalog Card No. 65–10168

For Sean Flannelly

eo. SCHOOLS
C607140

Acknowledgments

The author is grateful to Bernard F. Boyce, Assistant Secretary and Assistant Treasurer, Pinkerton's National Detective Agency, and to George F. O'Neill, Assistant Director, Public Relations, for making available to him valuable source material used in the writing of this book.

Contents

1. A Glasgow Boyhood   13

2. Escape to the New World   22

3. A Shrewd Yokel Becomes a Detective   35

4. Two Strange Cases—and One Suspicious
   Character   48

5. The Plot to Kill Abraham Lincoln   65

6. "Major Allen" Snares a Spy   79

7. Timothy Webster's Close Shaves   99

8. A Great Spy Dies, and the Reno Gang   109

9. A Chicago Murder and a Brooklyn Manhunt   128

10. A Pinkerton vs. the Molly Maguires   138

11. Baron Max and Handsome Walter   151

12. Jesse James   162

13. The King is Dead   177

    Bibliography   185

    Index   187

MASTER DETECTIVE
ALLAN PINKERTON

1 A Glasgow Boyhood

FOR THE FIFTH TIME THAT EVENING ISABELLA PINKERTON
went to the window to part the curtains and look out into
the cold November street. Sergeant Pinkerton, of the Glasgow
police, was long overdue.

Allan, twelve and youngest of the three Pinkerton boys,
put down the schoolbook he was making a pretense of study-
ing. "Mother," he said, "I'll go to the station house and ask
about father, if you like."

John, the eighteen-year-old, threw his brother an annoyed
look. "If anybody inquires, it's going to be me!" Robert, who
was sixteen, nodded; he always agreed with his elder brother.

Sighing, Mrs. Pinkerton left the window, returned to her
chair and took up her tatting again. She shook her head at
Allan. "Captain MacDonald doesn't like to be bothered by
the families of his men. We'll wait a bit. There's probably
nothing the matter; your father's been late before. Just last
week the Captain kept him till almost midnight, writing a
report on those—men he arrested."

An uneasy silence fell over the family gathered round the
kitchen fireplace. Allan broke it, mentioning the word his
mother had avoided using.

"Those men were Chartists, weren't they? Who are these
Chartists, anyway, and what do they stand for?"

13

He had addressed his mother, but it was John who answered him. "The Chartists are workingmen who are fighting for more rights and better pay. Not only here, in Glasgow, but all over the British Isles. And if you ask me, they deserve to be heard."

Mrs. Pinkerton was shocked. "John, you'll not talk that way in William Pinkerton's house! Why, at this very moment your father might be trading blows with a mob of these— these bloody revolutionists! And if Captain MacDonald ever heard you saying such things, he'd be very angry. . . ." Her words, which lacked conviction, trailed off indecisively. She was a woman of average intelligence, but politics and such matters were beyond her, and when called upon to discuss them she felt out of her depth.

But John didn't intend to let the matter drop. "For your information, Mother, Father has a lot of sympathy for the Chartist cause, even if he is a policeman, sworn to uphold law and order. And why? Because he knows injustice when he sees it. Injustice, and worse. Starving factory workers and colliers, not only in Scotland, but in Wales and England, too . . . children of twelve working sixteen hours a day . . . poorhouses, full of drafts and roaches, where old people are lucky to survive a week!"

Young Allan stared at his brother in fascination. For a draper's assistant, John certainly knew how to use the English language. And what he said seemed to make sense. If so many workingmen were up in arms and rioting, there must be good reason for it. Especially if his father saw some right on the Chartists' side.

There was a knock at the door, and Mrs. Pinkerton got to her feet so suddenly that her tatting fell to the floor.

"I'll answer it," said Allan. He opened the half-door to a policeman holding his top hat in his hands. With a cry Isabella Pinkerton rushed forward.

"What's wrong? Is it William, my husband?"

"It's Sergeant Pinkerton, ma'am," the policeman said regretfully. "He was hurt in the rioting on Argyle Street, and they took him to Glasgow Hospital. That was a couple of hours ago. Now he's in the van outside."

She ran to the horse-drawn hospital van at the curb. The boys followed her, Allan snatching up a shawl for his mother as he left the house.

Hospital attendants, directed by a doctor, were already lowering a stretcher from the van. William Pinkerton lay on it, pale and motionless.

They brought him into the bedroom. Then the doctor took Mrs. Pinkerton gently aside. He must, he told her, speak frankly. Her husband had been beaten and trampled by Chartist rioters, and his spine was badly damaged. It was doubtful he would ever recover the full use of his legs. The doctor had put him on sedatives for the moment.

Though Mrs. Pinkerton was stricken speechless, only one of the family, John, broke down and wept. Robert couldn't understand why, but Allan did.

"It's because John talked in favor of the Chartists," Allan told him later. "He feels bad about it."

Robert looked at him wonderingly. "You know a lot, don't you, for so wee a lad?"

"Not so wee," Allan answered him. "Anyway, I'll be leaving school now to go to work, and so will you, Rob. Father's pension won't take care of more than half the family expenses."

Robert sat down slowly as the import of Allan's words hit him. The wee lad was right.

Within a few weeks it had become evident that William Pinkerton would be an invalid for the rest of his life. He took it well, this upright Scot who had devoted his life to the

Glasgow force, and he had no bitterness in his heart for the
men who had maimed him.

"Men don't become wild animals for no reason," he told
Allan. "The Chartists have suffered much injustice, and it's
wrong that a man should be denied the vote because he owns
no property."

"I can't forgive them," Allan blurted out. Seeing his father
lying in bed day after day, in pain and helpless, had made
him come to hate the Chartist bullyboys and their brutal
methods. He swallowed. "I want to become a policeman, like
you, so I can pay them back."

His father smiled sadly. "My lad, revenge can make a career
for you, but never a life. Someday you'll understand what
I'm saying."

Allan didn't wait for his mother to tell him that he had to
quit school and go to work. One day he came back with a job
—errand boy for Neil Murphy, a pattern maker.

Murphy was a difficult employer—harsh, demanding and
often cruel. Allan yearned for the day when he could leave
him.

Still, there were compensations. Shut up in venture (grade)
school, he had never had an opportunity to see much of
Glasgow, and it proved a fascinating city. On High Street he
came across the plaque commemorating Wallace's defeat of
the English in the Battle o' the Brae in 1300, and in odd
moments of leisure between errands he walked in Queen's
Park, whose rich green turf had been trod by Mary Stuart.
He visited the workshop where James Watt had tinkered with
his steam engine, and his job took him as far as the handsome
mansions on the west side built on fortunes made in tobacco.

One summer night he came home tired from work and the
sharpness of Neil Murphy's tongue to find a visitor chatting
with his mother in the kitchen. The man was big and craggy-
featured, with a warm smile.

"Allan, this is Mr. McCauley," Mrs. Pinkerton said. "He's noticed how fast you run on your errands, and he'd like to know if you'd care to work for him as an apprentice."

"What's your trade, sir?" Allan asked politely.

"I'm a cooper, lad," McCauley told him. "I make barrels."

"Oh." If Mr. McCauley had been a policeman, the boy would have responded more enthusiastically, but he guessed law enforcement wasn't really a trade but a profession.

"Good barrels, lad," McCauley went on. "I know barrels don't sound all that interesting, but there's a lot of craft in the making. A tight barrel that doesn't leak is a work of art, in a manner of speaking. And it's made from good, sweet-smelling wood."

William Pinkerton called from the bedroom, and excusing herself, Mrs. Pinkerton left the room.

"Cooperage is a good business, lad," McCauley continued, "and after seven years of apprenticeship you'll be able to set up on your own. You'll not be a rich man, but at least your family won't want for the necessities. Come now, what do you say?"

Allan's practical side asserted itself. "What do you pay, Mr. McCauley?"

"To an apprentice, not much more than what your mother tells me Murphy is paying you now. But in a year or two, twelve shillings. I'm a Chartist, and no man or boy starves in my employ."

Allan got to his feet. "I won't work for a Chartist," he blurted out.

McCauley's eyes frosted over with anger, but then his look softened. "I know about your father, lad, and I understand . . . perhaps a little better than you do." He reached for his cap. "Suppose you take a few days to think it over? Have a talk with your father. It might help."

At the door he turned. "Your mother has my address, if you change your mind."

Though Allan did have a talk with his father, it wasn't anything that William Pinkerton said that changed his attitude toward working for William McCauley; it was the fact that Robert came home next day discharged from his job with the greengrocer's. Money for household expenses and medicines was needed immediately, so fighting down his fierce Scot pride, the boy went to work at the cooperage Monday morning.

Mr. McCauley kept him only half a day; somehow the craftsman had made it his business to find out that today, August 25, 1832, was Allan's thirteenth birthday. He's a decent sort, really, Allan told himself, munching a bannock on his way home. Even if he *is* a Chartist.

There was more to making barrels than he had thought. You had to cut staves so they showed no daylight when you put them together, and to fit a hoop around the lower end and make it stay was enough to try the patience of a saint. Working the windlass that tightened the rope which drew the top together was far from child's play, and the steaming of the wood, so it would bend to fit the hoops, required skill and application.

Allan didn't think he was starting off too well, but McCauley had only encouragement for him. "You learn quicker than most," he told the boy. "The only trouble is that your brain works faster than your hands can keep up with it."

"Do you mean I'm clumsy, sir?"

"Now did I say that?" McCauley said tactfully, and moved off toward the wood-steaming room.

Allan's fellow workers were all passionate Chartists who spent much of their free time discussing the glorious day when the revolutionary movement would sweep the British Isles.

"It's all a matter o' the vote," the men were fond of saying. Give him the vote, and every workingman would have a good house, decent clothes and enough food and drink to make him feel like a real human being.

It was little enough to ask for, Allan decided, and gradually he came around to the majority point of view. When William Pinkerton died the next year, in 1833, what anger the boy felt mixed with his grief was directed not at the Chartist ruffians who had put his father in his grave and prevented himself from getting an education; it was directed at the privileged and the injustice that had created the social conditions that made violence inevitable.

Shortly after his sixteenth birthday Allan began to attend Chartist meetings with his brother John, who was writing pamphlets and broadsides for the movement. Soon the boy was running errands for the leaders, and on one unforgettable occasion at headquarters he shook the hand of Henry Vincent, the movement's most famous orator. Allan's intelligence and enthusiasm caught the eye of the more important Chartists, and he was given more responsibility. By the age of eighteen he was second in command of a "physical force" battalion led by a tough River Clyde stevedore named Ian McDougall. McDougall, who had more courage than brains, depended upon the young cooper to plan riots and protests, and Allan was seldom home.

One Sunday evening he entered the house on Ruglen Loan to find Captain MacDonald waiting in the parlor. The policeman was in civilian clothes. Isabella Pinkerton avoided her son's eye, and Allan knew she had asked MacDonald here to talk to him.

"The Captain would like a few words with you," his mother said diffidently.

Allan poured himself a cup of tea and sat down. "In that case I'd suggest that he invite me to the station house."

MacDonald smiled. "Allan, I'm here unofficially."

"I don't take kindly to lectures, official or not," Allan told him.

"Let's not call it a lecture, but a bit of advice. Allan, you're doing well at McCauley's and in a few years you'll be able to set up on your own. You'll be marrying, raising a family. Why risk all that for a chance to play at brickbats and stones like any ordinary hooligan?"

"You wouldn't understand," Allan said, and buttered a scone.

"I won't bring up your father," MacDonald said quietly, "or what he would have said about the way you're headed. But I'll tell you this," and his voice firmed, "the police and the magistrates have orders to be harder on Chartists caught disturbing the peace." He paused. "I don't think a lad of your free and independent temperament would find jail very much fun."

Allan finished the scone and licked his fingers. "Captain, you don't scare me a bit. First you've got to catch me, and you haven't managed that yet. And there's no way you can get me fired, because William McCauley's against you and the bloodsucking rich who pay your salary."

MacDonald ignored the insult. "I'm not so blind as you think. A few weeks ago I saw you at the Salt Market pointing out to your hooligans what windows to smash. I could have had you arrested, but I thought of your mother. Next time will be a different matter."

He got up to go. Her eyes moist, Mrs. Pinkerton saw him to the door. When she turned round again, Allan was buttoning up his coat.

"Where are you going?" she asked him reproachfully. "To headquarters, I suppose. Can't you spend an evening at home?"

Allan kissed her on the forehead. "Rest easy. It isn't headquarters I'm bound for. I'm meeting a girl."

"A girl," she repeated, pleased. Allan was as closemouthed as his father, and never told her anything.

"What's her name, Allan?"

"Joan Carfrae. She lives on Dumfries Lane. Good night, Mother, don't wait up."

Isabella Pinkerton sighed as the door closed behind him. She had wanted to ask how long Allan had known this girl, and if he really liked her. Dumfries Lane was in the Gorbels, the Glasgow slums, but the Gorbels bred an occasional levelheaded lass, and such a lass could make a great difference in the life of a boy like Allan; she could be a stabilizing influence, make him settle down.

With all her heart she hoped that Joan Carfrae—it was a solid-sounding, old Scots name—was the right kind of girl and that Allan wasn't too far gone in his lawless ways to see it.

2 Escape to the New World

ALLAN HADN'T INTRODUCED JOAN CARFRAE TO HIS MOTHER for a good reason—she would have disapproved of her. Joan was a militant Chartist, one of the few working-class girls or women in Glasgow spirited and independent-minded enough to devote her free time and energy to a movement from which she stood to gain little or nothing for herself.

The daughter of a woolen millworker who was old before his time, Joan burned with anger at the economic exploitation that had aged her father prematurely and sent her overworked mother to an early grave.

She and Allan met at a Chartist meeting. He fell in love with the attractive eighteen-year-old on sight, and stared dumbly at her pretty face and soft brown hair until his brother John, with an elbow in the ribs, brought him back to reality. Later that evening Allan contrived to be introduced, and still later managed to walk her home to the shabby flat where she lived with her father and three brothers.

One of the things that charmed him about Joan was her complete indifference to material things. She had no self-consciousness about her threadbare clothes or her poor living conditions. She cared so passionately for justice and rights that the rest of the unpleasant world became less than important. Of course, such a cast of mind in a girl had its disadvantages, especially for the boy who felt attracted to her. When he asked Joan a personal question she would answer it briefly if at all and continue her discussion of how soon the organization would be able to call a general strike in Scotland.

She didn't ask him in to meet her family. It was late, and she had to rise at six in order to cook their breakfast and get ready for work at the factory.

"Will I see you again, Joan?" he asked her quickly. With a girl like this it was hard to know where you stood.

She looked at him, her eyes round. "Why Allan Pinkerton, you great ninny, of course you will—the next time you ask me! Don't you know you're the nicest boy I ever met? And the most impressive?"

She touched his cheek with a finger, and then she was gone.

He walked home whistling.

Though Allan Pinkerton was to be famed for his memory, he could seldom recall events of the period between 1837, the year he met Joan Carfrae, and 1842, the year he married her. Perhaps it was because he was in love and blind to anything but Joan and his work for Chartism; perhaps it was because nothing much actually happened. He put in his daily ten hours' work and saw Joan of an evening or dropped in at headquarters; then he went home to bed to prepare for another day at McCauley's.

Once, in one of the Glasgow police's periodic crackdowns, he was arrested and thrown into jail. But only for a day, until William McCauley appeared and paid his fine for him.

Shortly after his twenty-third birthday Allan and Joan were married in the Presbyterian Church. There was no possibility of a honeymoon; he couldn't afford it after furnishing the ground floor of a pleasant little house with a kitchen garden on Lansdown Lane.

They had just about settled in, the day after the wedding, when the knock at the door came that changed their lives.

It was Douglas Burns, one of Allan's Chartist colleagues.

"Headquarters hears there's a new wave of arrests sweeping north from Birmingham," Burns told him. "This time the Crown has a list of names, and ours are on it."

"Ours are on it, you say?" Allan said foggily. It was after midnight, and he and Joan had been asleep for only an hour.

"Man," said Burns impatiently, "don't you know what this means? A heavy jail sentence, unless we leave the country!"

His predicament was beginning to sink in. "Leave the country?" he said slowly. "But for where? I don't have a penny. It's all gone to furnish the house."

Burns took a wad of bank notes from his pocket. "The committee ticketed twenty pounds for you and Joan. With this you can get to Canada, by steamer."

"Allan, what is it?" Joan came into the room, rubbing her eyes. "Oh, Douglas. What brings you here at this hour?"

"Better tell her straightaway, Allan," Burns said grimly.

Joan took it well, even though it was a shock to leave behind all the new household goods they had shopped for so thriftily. As an engaged girl and then a married woman she had lost some of her rebellious idealism for the Chartist cause.

"When must we leave?" she asked Burns.

"As soon as possible. You'd better not sleep here tonight. Go to a hotel, or to Allan's mother's. There's a ship leaving for Halifax tomorrow afternoon."

"Will you come with us?" Allan asked him.

"No, I have a brother in Manchester." He grimaced. "I don't like living among the English, but a Scot in hiding has no choice."

The couple spent the night with Mrs. Pinkerton, a none too pleasant one due to her sighs and I-told-you-so's directed at Allan. The next morning they paid their fare and boarded the Halifax-bound steamer. There was no time for Joan to say good-by to her family or for Allan to shake William McCauley's hand.

It was only a two-week trip, but it seemed like an eternity. Had Allan been able to sell their furnishings before leaving Glasgow he and Joan would have traveled in comparative comfort, but they had only enough money for third-class tickets, plus a little left over. The purser assigned them hammocks in the crowded, ill-ventilated steerage.

Allan could stand the poor food, bad air and crowded living conditions, but it hurt him to see Joan enduring such squalor. He felt he should be able to provide for her better than this.

Joan hushed his self-reproaches. "We're bound for the New World, aren't we?" she asked him brightly. "You'll do well there, Allan, I know."

He told himself he was a very lucky man to have such a wonderful wife, but then he would catch sight of her face in an unguarded moment, and the fatigue and worry it showed made him blame himself for getting them into this fix. He couldn't call himself a very good husband, not when he was responsible for making her leave family, home and country when he had promised to cherish and protect her against the hostile world. It didn't help to remind himself that she was—or had been—as ardent a revolutionary as he.

During the day the steerage passengers had nowhere to sit but in the space that was left vacant by their slung hammocks. The men were accustomed to going off in groups to dice and play cards, but Allan, who preferred to spend his time reading one of the books he had brought with him, stayed close to his bride.

One of the young couple's neighbors was Owen McClintoch, a mild, bespectacled clerk who seemed an unlikely candidate for the rigors of emigration. Like most mild-mannered men in circumstances that did not favor his breed, McClintoch had managed to find his bully during the trip. This bully was the steerage steward, a red-faced Irishman named Sweeney.

Sweeney was less steward than below-decks policeman and disciplinarian. Harsh and short-tempered with the people he was supposed to serve, he ruled the steerage like a tyrant. Allan knew he and the Irishman would come to blows before the steamer docked at Halifax.

Owen McClintoch furnished the occasion. The Irishman, making his rounds, stumbled over the clerk's rather big feet. Hauling the terrified man up by the scruff of his neck, he cuffed him so hard that McClintoch's spectacles flew off and smashed against a bulkhead.

The next thing Sweeney knew he was on his knees, beaten to the deck by the fists of heavy-set Allan Pinkerton.

"Pick on a defenseless mon, will ye?" Allan shouted. "I'll teach ye to respect a mon because he's a mon, not just because he's got a fat wallet in his pocket!" In his rage and excitement the Glasgow burr of his boyhood had slipped back into his speech.

Sweeney got to his feet slowly, and the watching crowd of emigrants drew back. His small pig eyes were hard and mean. Wiping a thread of blood from his mouth he muttered, "Pinkerton, you'll pay for this," and elbowed his way through the onlookers to the companionway.

Tauntingly Allan called after him: "If anybody's going to pay for anything, you big bag of wind, it's you! For a new pair of spectacles!" The crowd laughed.

Allan was a hero, but he expected a summons from the Captain, and it came. An hour later he was called to his cabin. He went docilely enough; he had promised Joan not to make any trouble.

Captain Hodges was a thin man with pinched nostrils. He

was evidently used to steerage troublemakers, and gave Allan short shrift.

"Pinkerton, your name is? Well, Pinkerton, there'll be no more fights. Lay another finger on Steward Sweeney, and we'll clap you in the brig till we dock at Halifax."

Allan ignored the threat. "Sir," he said, "it's only justice that McClintoch gets a new pair of spectacles."

The Captain looked at him impatiently. "What are you raving about? Who's McClintoch?"

Allan identified the clerk and explained that the episode was entirely Sweeney's fault, but it was plain the Captain preferred to take the steward's word for what had happened. "So far as I'm concerned," he said, "you attacked Sweeney when he tripped over your foot. Now I've wasted enough time with the likes of you—"

"Sir," Allan interrupted evenly, "there are witnesses. If you don't believe me, ask them. It's only justice."

The Captain slammed his fist down on the desk. "What's all this talk of justice! You sound like one of those confounded revolutionaries! Yes, now that I think of it, you're probably a Chartist. That's it, isn't it, Pinkerton? Yes, I see it on your face. Well, now that I've your number, here's fair warning. Any more trouble, and it's back to Glasgow for you, in irons, to face whatever charges the police have against you!"

Allan reminded himself he was a married man, with a young wife to take care of. He would have to forget McClintoch's spectacles.

"Well, man, do you have anything to say?" demanded the Captain.

"No, sir."

"Then get back to where you belong."

He avoided Sweeney for the rest of the trip, and fortunately the cowardly steward was equally careful. But it wasn't easy, seeing the nearsighted McClintoch stumbling about the steerage, bumping into things and people. It made Allan want to twist Sweeney's arm until the bully agreed to do right by his friend.

Before the voyage ended Allan had a second, if less serious, brush with authority. Unlike the other steerage passengers he and Joan were curious about what life in the first and second classes was like, and though it was strictly forbidden, one afternoon Allan put on his best suit and, slipping beneath the chain, made his way to the deck above.

Second class wasn't too impressive, though the passengers had separate cabins and a lounge. Most of them were dressed no better than he, and he sat down in the lounge and ordered a cup of tea with perfect self-assurance.

First class, though, was different. The corridors were richly carpeted, and a huge crystal chandelier hung in the lounge. A string quartet was playing, and he must have stood there gawking like a greenhorn at the lovely women and well-fed men, because a purser who had been eyeing him suspiciously came up and tapped him lightly on the shoulder.

"Sir," he said, "do you have a second-class ticket?"

Allan swallowed. The man might ask him for his papers, and he had a terrible picture of Captain Hodges tossing him into the brig. "I—" he began, and tensed himself to run.

"Second-class passengers aren't allowed on the top deck. Now if you'll kindly go below?"

Allan moved off toward the companionway. It hadn't been as bad as all that, but he couldn't help thinking bitterly how it was this best suit of his that had saved him from what could have been trouble. Justice, even on the high seas, was still a matter of your bank account and social standing.

The steamer was due to dock in Halifax harbor on the morning of November 12. By that afternoon it was still at sea, rolling through rough waters and heavy fog. No explanation was given to the steerage passengers, crouched around their pitiful possessions and ready to disembark.

At the dot of four, there was a sudden rending crash. The ship listed sickeningly to one side, and water began pouring into the hold. The screaming of the women and children was terrible.

"We must have hit a rock," Allan told the terrified Joan, and picking up their two suitcases, he plunged ahead toward the companionway that led topside.

Fighting his way there with Joan clinging to the belt of his overcoat, he happened to glance behind him and saw Owen McClintoch, knocked to his knees, feeling around blindly for his belongings. The clerk would never survive the wreck without help.

Allan handed Joan the lighter of the suitcases. "Get into a boat as quickly as you can," he told her. "If the valise is troublesome, leave it behind."

"Allan, don't leave me!" Joan begged, but before she could remonstrate with him further he had begun to push back through the hysterical crowd toward McClintoch.

When Allan looked toward the companionway again Joan had disappeared. A cursing, screaming mass of humanity was crowding around the companionway entrance, fighting to get through. By now the water was almost knee deep, and the ship listed even more alarmingly to starboard.

Clutching Owen's arm, Allan hurried him in the opposite direction, toward the steerage mess and the door there that led above.

"Why are ye doin' this, lad?" McClintoch gasped. "Ye should be with your lass."

"She's a strong girl. Save your breath, Owen," Allan told him, and pushed on.

No one else had thought of getting above by means of the mess companionway, and Allan and Owen soon found themselves topside among the second-class passengers. Crewmen were lowering boats; other boats were already beating their way toward shore in the lifting fog. In one of them Allan thought he could see Joan in her green plaid coat.

Twenty minutes later the two Scots were huddled around a fire on the beach, drinking tea brewed for them by the people of Sable Island. The pilot had run aground there, two hundred miles off his course. Through the wisps of fog the rescued could see the steamer lying at an angle, with a huge gash in her hull. She had made her last Atlantic run.

The disaster, Allan learned, could have been much more serious; so far no drownings had been reported, though there were several injuries and cases of exposure. The islanders urged Allan to get thoroughly dried out before he began to search for Joan, but when he finished his tea he threw off the blankets and ran down the beach.

He found her a few hundred yards away, steaming out before one of the fires. They spent the night as guests of a kind island couple, and in the morning took stock of their resources—two suitcases of damp clothes, and exactly $55.28.

Joan refused to be discouraged. "At least it's enough to get us to Vancouver, our destination."

"We're not going to Vancouver," Allan told her. "I've a feeling about Canada. If we stay here it will mean only more bad luck. I'd rather head for Detroit, across the border. And besides—" he hesitated.

"Go on, Allan."

"I'd like to give Owen McClintoch enough for a new pair of spectacles. He's lost without them. If we do that, we wouldn't have enough money for Vancouver."

Joan sighed. "As you wish, though I just hope we don't meet up with too many other poor Scots in need of a helping hand. We need a helping hand ourselves."

By schooner they reached the St. Lawrence, and via the

Great Lakes arrived at Detroit. Allan could find no work there, and with about the last of their money bought a horse and wagon for the trek further West. He and Joan had agreed to try Chicago. They arrived there in late December, after numerous stopovers in towns where the young cooper replenished his funds by repairing casks and barrels.

Chicago had only recently received its charter as a city. The streets were dirty roads, except where there were planks called "corduroy roads." Spring rains and the melting that followed the winter freeze-up turned them into quagmires. Wagons sank up to their hubs in mud and pedestrians used planks to get from one side of the street to the other. The city nonetheless was a boomtown, teeming with land speculators who would rather see their children go hungry than miss out on a choice lot. About the only people who didn't live from hand to mouth were the frugal Scots. Knowing that the Scots in America were more than willing to aid a fellow countryman, Allan called on Robert Fergus, a printer, and asked if he know of any coopering work.

"Aye, lad, there's some to be found at Lill's Brewery. We print their labels for 'em. But I don't know that the pay's so good; it's a smallish company."

The pay at Lill's was barely adequate—fifty cents a day— but Allan accepted it gratefully. With a regular weekly paycheck made out to Allan Pinkerton, cooper, Joan could forget her talk about taking in washing.

Within a year the couple had pulled up stakes and moved thirty-eight miles northwest to the Scots settlement of Dundee. The small town of five hundred on the Fox River offered several advantages over city living. It was in the country; food and rent were cheap; and best of all Allan could go into business for himself, a necessity now that Joan was pregnant. With the help of neighbors he set up a workshop in the basement of his one-story frame house, a few hundred yards

from the river, and hung out a sign reading: "ALLAN PINKER-
TON, THE ONLY AND ORIGINAL COOPER OF DUNDEE."

In the years to come he was more than once to bless
William McCauley for giving him the chance to learn the
cooper's trade. A Chartist agitator in America with no special
skills would have had a very difficult time.

Four years after he and Joan had crossed the Canadian
border into the United States, he had a livelihood, a house
and garden, a young son, William, and a respected place in a
pleasant community.

Though Allan still had a weather eye out for injustice to
the workingman, his interest in politics had shifted from
revolution to Abolitionism, the legal extinction of Negro
slavery. Chartism had failed in Great Britain, but this, after
all, was the United States.

He had a young German assistant, Wilhelm Schultz, and
was able to leave the shop occasionally to cut poles and staves
in the uninhabited land upriver.

One afternoon he rowed out to a small Fox River island.
To his surprise he saw that a number of people had camped
there recently. More interesting than that was the fact that
they had tried to erase signs of their presence. The charred
embers of a campfire were scattered about, and footprints,
including those of a woman, showed plainly in the mud by
the water's edge. Near the former campsite Allan found half
of a burned five-dollar bill.

He sat down on a log to think. These were no ordinary
people who had visited here. A family from Dundee wouldn't
have found it necessary to hide traces of a campsite on an
uninhabited island. That being the case, the campers had
been illicit. Kane County of late had been plagued by horse
thieves, coiners and counterfeiters—counterfeiters, that was
it! He picked up the charred bill again. Who but a counter-

feiter would, in a moment of bravado, light his cigar with a bogus bill?

Quickly he cut a number of hoop poles, threw them into the boat and rowed back to Dundee. A short time later he was telling his story to B. C. Yates, the sheriff of Kane County.

The sheriff doubted his interpretation. "This bill looks too genuine," he objected.

"I'll bet you five dollars it's counterfeit."

"Neither of us have that kind of money to throw around, but suppose we send the bill to the Chicago police and see what they say?"

Allan shook his head doggedly. "That'll take at least two weeks, Sheriff. You know how slow the Chicago police can be. Why not put a watch on the island? I'll bet you another five dollars those counterfeiters will be back—and soon."

"What makes you say that?"

"I read that a lot of counterfeit money was passed in Chicago just last week. After they pass a wad these crooks lay low for a while, don't they? What better hideout could they have than Fox River?"

The sheriff knew he would have no peace until he gave in. The bill was sent to Chicago, and a night watch put on the island. The third night a bone-chilled deputy saw a campfire and rowed back to Dundee with the news. A posse was organized and dispatched. It returned with four men and a woman, a press and special inks used in counterfeiting. The criminals implicated three confederates, who were picked up later in a Chicago rooming house.

Allan Pinkerton became a local hero overnight. The counterfeiter's hideout received a name—Bogus Island.

Eight days after the gang was returned to Chicago for trial, Sheriff Yates received word from the Chicago experts that the charred five-dollar bill was "definitely counterfeit."

"I wired Chicago asking if you could keep the bill as a

souvenir," he told Allan, "but they said the government plans to use it as evidence."

Allan grinned. "That's all right, Sheriff. I guess I'll have to make my satisfaction do. You see, I always wanted to be a policeman."

"The force lost a good man. But maybe it's not too late, Allan. I'd like to come by, say once a week, and discuss my problems with you. I'm sure you'll have some good ideas and suggestions."

Allan told him he was welcome to drop in any time he pleased.

3 A Shrewd Yokel Becomes a Detective

CO. SCHOOLS
C607140

SEVERAL WEEKS WENT BY WITHOUT YATES PUTTING IN AN appearance, but then he dropped by with a real problem.

A prosperous Scot named George Smith had established a bank in Milwaukee. It was, at this time, legal for banks to issue their own bills in various denominations, and the farmers of Wisconsin and Illinois had put these George Smith notes into steady circulation. They were described as being "good as wheat." Recently, however, bank notes excellently counterfeiting those of Smith had been turning up in Kane County. A good many of them were passing into the hands of Dundee's two storekeepers, Joseph Hunt and Increase Bosworth, and the businessmen faced ruin.

There could be only one explanation for the presence of so much counterfeit money in Dundee—the maker was a resident of the town. Yates' suspicions centered on Henry Crane, a hard character whose small, unproductive farm hardly explained his evident prosperity. In recent weeks several strangers had come through town asking to be directed to Crane's farm. More damningly yet, Crane was known to be entertaining two guests, men with a city look about them. It was Yates' considered opinion that these men were engravers. Customers wouldn't have stayed so long.

"What's your plan, Sheriff?" Allan asked him. "To raid

Crane's farm in the hopes of pinning the goods on him?"

Yates shook his head. "I can't do that; no way of getting a search warrant on present evidence. I'll have to wait till someone else comes through town looking for him, and I can use the fellow to get information that'll eventually put Crane in jail."

"And that's where I come in?"

"Right, Allan. I can't do the job, not with sheriff written all over me. Are you game?"

Allan grinned and, falling into his burlesque Scots dialect, burred: "Nay, an' if I refused ye, what would me dear murther say?"

The opportunity to pursue the Crane investigation wasn't long in coming. One afternoon a well-dressed stranger stopped his carriage at Eaton Walker's local harness shop with a broken girth and casually inquired the way to Henry Crane's. Every tradesman in Dundee had been told by Sheriff Yates what to say and do should he be asked that question. Pretending ignorance of Crane's whereabouts, Eaton Walker returned to his work, but not before whispering terse instructions to his young apprentice. Seconds later the apprentice was on his way to the county jail, where Sheriff Yates had his office, and in less than twenty minutes Allan Pinkerton, dressed in dirty coveralls and chewing a wisp of hay, sauntered in the door.

To the stranger this yokel, with his wide grin and vacant eyes, looked as if he didn't know enough to come in out of a hailstorm. Still, the hayseed had probably lived in Dundee all his life.

"You," the stranger addressed Allan, "do you know the way to Henry Crane's?"

The yokel scratched his head. "Pretty far out, Crane's place is. But I reckon I can find it."

"I'll give you a dollar to take me there."

The yokel's eyes lit up. "You mean that, mister?"

Not bothering to answer such a foolish question, the stranger shouted to Walker to hurry up his work.

The saddler reappeared with the mended leather band, and the visitor, though he showed a thick bankroll, paid him in hard coin. "Let's be off," he said to Allan impatiently. "I want to be at Crane's by dusk."

As they rode toward the outskirts of town the stranger introduced himself as John Craig, from Vermont. He was commanding in appearance, and had the keenest, coldest small gray eyes Allan Pinkerton had ever seen. On his own part, Craig soon discovered that his companion was double the rube he had taken him for, and the most loquacious rustic ever. The fellow rattled on about his family, his relations and his financial problems, until Craig fairly drooped in his saddle from boredom. Times were bad, his crop was poor this year. His father-in-law, a Scotsman and tight as a well-made barrel, refused to be co-signer for a bank loan that he needed desperately. For two cents he would throw up farming entirely and go into something else. Maybe barrel-making, said to be a good trade.

John Craig was on the lookout for good prospects for get-rich-quick schemes, especially in the sticks. Farmers, he had learned, were more vulnerable than the more skeptical city dweller to a promise of something for practically nothing. He stopped his carriage and took from his pocket the roll of bills he had flashed in the saddlery. Peeling off the top one, a five-dollar bill, he handed it to his guide.

Sheriff Yates had shown Allan some of the counterfeit bills passed off on Hunt and Bosworth. This was another "George Smith" counterfeit, its quality and workmanship inferior to those of bills passed in Dundee.

"Take a careful look," Craig said. "Does that bill look bogus to you?"

"Sure doesn't," lied Allan.

"Well, I can sell you lots of this bang-up stuff, if you've got the real money to pay for it."

"Maybe I can get the money," Allan said, letting a shrewd look come into his eye. "There's plenty of men in this town wouldn't mind getting into a good thing."

"No questions asked, either?"

"No questions, if I can show them what they're getting."

The Vermonter pondered for a moment, then giddapped to his horse. Half an hour later, when they were on the main road through the woods, he reigned in. He took the bankroll from his pocket and peeled off about a hundred dollars worth of bills.

"Show this to your friends. My price is twenty-five per cent in good bills for five hundred dollars in counterfeit—that comes to a hundred and twenty-five dollars."

Allan pocketed the bogus. "I'll have the good bills for you by tomorrow. Where do you want to meet, at Crane's?"

Craig shook his head definitely. "Henry would skin me alive if he knew I was doing business with anybody else in Dundee. He's a cautious man."

Allan pondered for a moment. "There's a half-built Baptist church about two miles south of Dundee. We could meet there."

They agreed on a time and resumed the journey. Some three miles later, at the crossroads on the other side of the woods, Allan said good-by to his new business partner. Crane's house was only a quarter-mile down the road.

Sheriff Yates was pleased with the job Allan had done so far, and called an immediate meeting with Hunt and Bosworth. The merchants were willing to donate $125 between them toward the eventual arrest of Craig in the hope that it would lead to Henry Crane's undoing. But they could raise

no additional capital. Allan told them he would do his best
with what he had.

Next afternoon, at the Baptist church, Craig turned over
an additional $400 in counterfeit notes and pocketed the $125
in good "George Smith," whose serial numbers had been
carefully noted by the sheriff.

Craig seemed impressed that Allan had raised the money
so quickly. "Young fellow," he told him, "I'm on my way
to Chicago tomorrow. You want to do some more business in
the next two weeks, just look me up at the Sauganash House."

Allan nodded. "Did Crane have any good stuff for you?"
he asked innocently.

Craig shrugged. "I only bought a couple of hundred dollars worth. One of his engravers lit out on him, and his new
stuff is pretty mediocre. Crane can't match the workmanship
of other fellows in Illinois. This state's just running over
with first-class counterfeiters."

"Well, I just might look you up in Chicago," Allan said,
and the two men shook hands and parted.

Hunt and Bosworth raised an additional thirty-five dollars
to send Allan to Chicago. When he knocked at Craig's hotel
room door a week later, dressed in loud country duds that
made the desk clerk titter, the Vermonter took his presence
as a matter of course and immediately got down to business.

"I'll give you six thousand dollars of good bogus for one
thousand dollars of genuine George Smith or any other
reputable currency. That's a better deal than you got before.
But I've got to have your money in an hour."

"Sounds good," Allan said. "The only thing is, my partner's here in town with me, and he'll want to see your
bundle."

"This man holding your money?" Craig asked shrewdly.

Allan nodded. "He's got more than twelve hundred dollars
in his swag."

"How soon can you produce him?"

"Oh, in a couple of hours. Two, at the most."

Craig considered for a moment, smiled. "All right. I'll take a later train."

Allan returned with two policemen and a warrant for Craig's arrest. The counterfeiter, though caught red-handed with over ten thousand dollars of bogus money on him, took the matter calmly. When he and Allan were alone, he said, "All right, you must want Crane. I'm ready to talk if you'll refuse to testify against me in Chicago."

Allan shook his head. "I can't do that, Mr. Craig. But I'll go as easy on you as I can."

Craig accepted his conditions.

There were no legal secretaries at the primitive Chicago police station, and Allan had to go out and hire a lawyer, on the understanding that Hunt and Bosworth would pay his fee later on. The lawyer took down an affidavit that would put Henry Crane behind bars for at least five years, and Allan left with it for Dundee.

Sheriff Yates had the pleasure of calling on Crane with a warrant for his arrest. Counterfeiting equipment worth thousands of dollars was confiscated at Crane's farm, and the counterfeiter himself was locked up in Dundee's two-room jail until he could produce bail.

The bail was forthcoming, but Henry Crane never came to trial. He sold his farm and skipped the country with his family. Nor did John Craig pay the price of his illegal dealings. Hunt and Bosworth had decided it wasn't their responsibility to send Allan Pinkerton back to Chicago to testify against him.

The Dundee merchants, in fact, had tired of their role as public benefactors. They were several hundred dollars out of pocket, with no likelihood of getting it back.

"How much counterfeit have you?" Allan asked them.

"Two hundred twenty-five dollars worth," Increase Bosworth told him.

"That's almost exactly what you spent on the Crane case," Allan said. "If you'll send me to Milwaukee, I'll get it back for you."

Joseph Hunt was incredulous. "How?" he wanted to know.

"From George Smith himself," Allan answered. "I hear he's a public-spirited man. He'll approve of what you've done in Dundee."

The merchants were dubious, but finally agreed to take the gamble. At home, Allan discovered that Joan was something less than elated about his forthcoming trip.

"Look at all the time you've spent on this business already," she objected. "And what have you got to show for it?"

Allan admitted he had never thought of the matter in that light. The Crane case had interested him, and he had enjoyed working on it so much that the question of his own profit or loss hadn't entered his mind.

No, to be perfectly truthful, he couldn't quite say that. Riding back from Crane's that day he had been tempted for a moment to keep part of the bogus money for himself. He could have gotten away with it, merely by telling Yates and the merchants that Craig's discount was smaller than it actually was. And it had taught him a lesson: that the dividing line between the so-called honest man and the criminal could be thin as an eyelash.

Joan relented. "I guess it's the policeman in your blood, Allan. Go to Milwaukee, and good luck."

Allan returned in triumph. George Smith had listened to his story in silence, and then said, "I've just this to say, young man: ye was not authorized to do the work ye did, and ye have no right to a cent. I'll replace the counterfeit with good money, but mind ye now," and he shook his finger, "if ye ever do work for me agin that ye have no authorization fer, ye'll get ne'er a penny!" Allan left Milwaukee with the impression that Smith was not a little flattered that Henry Crane and others had gone to such trouble to counterfeit "his" money.

To show their gratitude, Hunt and Bosworth gave Allan a gift of ten dollars. As a reward it was less than munificent, considering that in expelling Henry Crane from Kane County Allan had sacrificed over ten times that amount in business he could ill afford to lose.

But he did gain in prestige. For miles around people spoke in awed tones of the young cooper who singlehanded had made Dundee an unsafe place for bad money and those who manufactured it. So smart a man, they thought, must be a very fine cooper. Within a few months Allan's business had increased threefold, and he had to enlarge his shop and hire several helpers.

Some of these helpers were Negroes. This itself was surprising in Dundee, where no Negroes lived. But Dundee was to find it even more surprising, during the years 1844–1847, that Allan Pinkerton, having hired out-of-town Negroes, should then have so constant a turnover in his help. A Negro who worked for the cooper didn't work for him very long. One day he was sweating in the steam room; the next day he had vanished.

Few citizens of Dundee knew the reason for this: that Allan Pinkerton was an ardent Abolitionist, and his cooperage shop was one of the busiest Underground Railroad stations in Illinois.

But the Pinkerton workshop was more than a station. Allan felt that an enemy of slavery should do more than merely pass on to safety, in Canada, runaway slaves and their families. He should, if such was within his power, teach a man to earn his living. Every Negro who expressed an interest in becom-

ing a barrelmaker was taught the trade, and at the expense
of the Dundee cooper.

Prominent Illinois Abolitionists called on Allan Pinkerton
with thanks for his work. These men knew the risk the
Underground Railroad foreman ran, not only to his pocket-
book but to his own freedom. In Illinois aiding and abetting
runaway slaves was a criminal offense. When B. C. Yates
appointed Allan deputy sheriff of Kane County in 1846, he
had to overlook the fact that if any proslaver in the county
chose to inform state authorities of his deputy's activities, the
Scot could go to jail.

Allan's Abolitionist work came to a temporary halt, but
not because of nosey local Copperheads. One day, six months
after he had joined Yates' office, a visitor called on the deputy
and made him a proposal.

Allan discussed it with Joan that night. Sheriff William
Church of Cook County wanted him to come to Chicago as a
special agent. He would have no particular title, and he
would be doing police work of various kinds. The salary was
only adequate, but his future looked bright—he might eventually succeed Church himself, who was already in his sixties.

What did she think? He could leave the business in charge
of Wilhem Schultz, his first employee and a good man. Someday Wilhelm might be able to buy him out. The real question was: did Joan want to leave Dundee, which they and
young Bill had come to love, for city living? Especially now
that she was expecting another child?

Joan was looking at him narrowly, and he asked her,
"What's the matter?"

"It's just that you're talking straight English, without a
hint of Scots. And whenever you get excited, as I know you
are now, your burr is always thick enough to cut with a
carving knife. Or used to be."

"My dear," he said impatiently, "this is a very important matter. It means our future lives. Don't joke with me."

"I'm not joking, Allan. If you'll let me finish, I was going to add this—that at last you've stopped being a Glasgow cooper and become a Chicago blue, a policeman."

Allan clasped her to him. "And you won't miss Dundee too much?"

"Not if I have you to miss it with me."

The Pinkertons settled on Adams Street in a two-story frame house surrounded by a colorful flower garden. Allan went to work investigating murders, burglaries and mundane stabbings. The Chicago Post Office borrowed him as a special agent, and he was busy with postal work—fraud, extortion and blackmail cases—until a new project developed: the organization of a regular police department from the loosely knit constabulary of Chicago. Special Agent Pinkerton's suggestions and recommendations came to fifty closely written pages. As a result of their excellence, and of his growing reputation, he was named the first detective on the Chicago force. He was also the only one.

The Chicago police were accustomed to doing things the easy way, springing into decisive action only when newspaper editorials demanded it, after some particularly shocking assault, burglary or murder. Policemen stuck comfortably to the station houses, putting in more time on cards and beer-drinking than criminal-catching. As a sop to their conscience, a horse-drawn van was kept ready at every station in anticipation of an alarm. The horses were well cared for and beautifully curried and combed. The Chicago force could claim it had the most impressive horses in the nation. But it could claim little else.

Detective Pinkerton didn't make himself unpopular by loudly criticizing the status quo, but he did operate in a way that showed the quiet contempt he had for it. He went to work early and came home late. He worked a full Saturday. Joan soon gave up waiting for him with dinner; his day might be over at one or two in the morning. He never seemed to tire. Bulldoglike, his short, heavy-set frame endlessly absorbed the punishment of long hours and dangerous assignments. On one of these he disarmed a knife-wielding madman who had badly cut two policemen; on another he hid behind the counter of a dry goods store for three days until the burglars he awaited showed up. He got them, but also a crick in the back that took six months to disappear.

Allan Pinkerton's name began to appear in the newspapers so often as an arresting officer that Chicagoans, used to their lackluster law enforcement, began to joke that this Pinkerton was nothing more than a clever figment of Sheriff Church's imagination. One newspaper challenged him to "come forward in the flesh."

When Detective Pinkerton, posing as a ticket agent for the Rock Island Railroad, solved a series of embezzlements that had John F. Tracy, its president, tearing his hair, the arrest wasn't reported in the Chicago papers. President Tracy was reluctant to let his other ticket agents learn the clever manner in which one of them had mulcted the company of five thousand dollars.

Tracy did ask the detective to drop by for a talk. He had to ask twice. Detective Pinkerton was too busy.

Finally, on a day in March, 1850, the two met. Tracy, it developed, had more than gratitude on his mind. He had a suggestion—that Allan Pinkerton go into private business. He and two other railroad presidents were prepared to set him up in a detective agency of his own if he would agree to investigate a number of railroad robberies. These robberies had been frequent and serious of late; petty and accomplished thieves had taken advantage of the vulnerability of railroads spread over rough and thinly settled country.

"We'll make it worth your while, Pinkerton," Tracy urged him. "We'll guarantee you ten thousand a year to protect our property. You'll be able to hire enough employees to go into other kinds of detective work. And now's the time to go into the agency business in Chicago, if you're going to, when there's practically no competition."

Allan thanked him. "I'd like to be on my own as much as any man. But this would mean quite a bit of traveling, and I see little enough of my wife and family as it is. You know we just had twins—a boy and a girl," he added proudly.

"All the more reason to get established in a business for yourself. But there's more to consider here than just a change of job. Railroads are the greatest thing that ever happened to this country. And they're here to stay. The man with money in railroad stock can make a fortune. I'll see you get your share of the Rock Island's choicest stock issues."

"Somehow I've never been much interested in making a lot of money, Mr. Tracy," Allan confessed to him.

Tracy waved a well-manicured hand. "Well, you'll change your mind. But don't take too long with your decision. Just last week we had a ten-thousand-dollar robbery outside of Cairo."

Joan was in favor of the agency. She argued that as a private detective he couldn't be any busier than he was now, and backed by the powerful railroad interests, the agency offered a possibility of future security that city hall, subject to political winds of ill fortune, could not. Besides, Wilhelm Schultz had just bought the cooperage business in Dundee for three thousand dollars, and if the agency was unsuccessful, they could fall back on that.

"You're the practical one," Allan admitted. "All I could think of was looking up at my sign with 'Pinkerton's National Detective Agency' on it. I've been thinking of a trademark— a wide-open eye."

"That sounds fine, but don't you need something else with it?"

"Something else?"

"Well, a slogan." She thought for a moment, finger to chin, and then snapped her fingers. "I've got it. 'We Never Sleep.' "

Allan looked at his wife wonderingly. She was thirty-one now, and there were traces of gray in her hair, but Joan Carfrae Pinkerton was just as slim and attractive as she had been on that night thirteen years ago when he had walked her home to the Gorbels. And, he thought admiringly, twice as clever.

"Do you like my slogan?" Joan asked impatiently.

Allan pursed his lips and shrugged like a cautious Scot who never accepts a new idea without giving it plenty of skeptical thought. "Waal, now," he said in broad Scots, "I'll ha' to gi' it sum-at of consideration. It might do, an' then agin it might not."

Joan threw a pillow at him, which struck a vase on the table, knocking it shatteringly to the floor. The noise woke the children, four-year-old William, and the new twins, Robert and Joan. They set up a terrific howl.

"Now look what you've done," Joan accused him. "They'll be up for hours."

" 'We Never Sleep,' " he said approvingly. "I like it."

Laughing, arms around each other, they went upstairs to cope with the family emergency.

4 Two Strange Cases—and One Suspicious Character

A NUMBER OF EX-POLICEMEN WHO KNEW ALLAN PINKERTON from his days on the force assumed they would go to work for him at his new agency; after all, who else in Chicago with any experience in law enforcement was available?

They were, to a man, mistaken. Detective Pinkerton interviewed them courteously enough at his secondhand rolltop desk in the small, crowded offices on Washington Street, but he gave them all the same answer: No.

Two of them were foolish enough to ask why. To the first the detective replied: "Why, O'Kelly? Well, to be frank with you, you're a drinker."

The Irishman looked at him in amazement. "What's wrong with a little snort?" he asked indignantly.

"Nothing, but your definition of a little drink is different from mine. I want a man who's always sober. A man under the influence, smart as he is, can't *think*."

To the second man who asked why, he answered: "It's the company you keep, Browning. You consort with known criminals, and you don't care who knows it."

Browning was genuinely offended. "How are you going to know what a crook's up to unless you're friendly with him? Sure, I have an occasional dram with the boys, but that doesn't mean I wouldn't turn one in if I had to."

48

"Would you take a bribe?"

"Of course I would!" said Browning stoutly. "There isn't a man alive who wouldn't, if a bribe is big enough."

"Well, I disagree. I don't think I would, and I don't want any man on my payroll who thinks it's only human nature to take what he can get, whether or not it's right for him to take it. In any contest between a crook and an honest man, the honest man is going to win out; and the more honest he is, the sooner he'll win out."

Browning got to his feet. There was a frankly contemptuous expression on his face. "You want angels, Pinkerton, not men."

"I don't think so," the detective told him. "I just want honest men."

He thought he had found nine honest men who wanted to work for the agency, and he hired them. He was confident all would follow Pinkerton's National's rules and regulations, known as his "General Principles," to the letter.

These "General Principles" survived as a code of practice which was never knowingly flouted by Allan Pinkerton or any agency representative during his lifetime. The printed "Principles" were suitably framed and hung over his operatives' desks. From time to time, as events and experience dictated, they were brought up to date, but they were never changed essentially.

The agency would not represent a defendant in a criminal case, except with the knowledge and consent of the prosecutor. It would not shadow jurors or investigate public officials in the performance of their duties. It would not hire informants, or stool pigeons; unlike the police of Europe and America, Allan Pinkerton did not believe "it takes a thief to catch a thief."

It would not accept employment from one political party against another. It would not work for vice crusaders. It would not accept divorce cases. In too many states, because of the peculiarity of the divorce laws, fabrication of evidence and collusion were employed, and Allan Pinkerton refused to be party to a situation which he regarded as a disgrace.

A fixed sum of three dollars was set as the cost of one Pinkerton operative on a per diem, or daily, basis. A client need pay only this amount, along with travel or other expenses agreed on in advance.

No Pinkerton detective could ever accept a gratuity from a client in advance of entering into an investigation, on the grounds that the detective might be tempted to "frame" evidence on behalf of the client. In reporting evidence, an operative must include everything favorable to the suspect as well as what was unfavorable to him.

Neither Allan Pinkerton nor any of his employees could increase the number of operatives at work on a case without advance notice to the client and without receiving from the client approval of such an increase. In some instances a wealthy client might give the agency a free hand from the beginning, but this privilege was not to be abused.

Pinkerton agents were not permitted to publish details of their experience in newspaper or magazine articles, on the theory that the privacy of clients would be invaded and that such details might help the criminal to escape if the case were a current one.

Addiction to liquor, tobacco and card-playing were forbidden, and operatives were not permitted to frequent "low dives." "Somber dress" was required at all times.

These were fine principles, too fine not to amuse Allan Pinkerton's former colleagues on the Chicago force. Many Chicago blues said flatly that such a detective agency wouldn't last six months. Pinkerton was hedging himself in with so many no's that he would never get enough yes's to pay the bills. No divorce cases! No informants! No investigation of public officials! No bribes! Where did the man exist who wouldn't take a bribe if you made it worth his while? You wouldn't find him in Chicago!

For a while the Scot's critics seemed justified in their doleful predictions. The detective did so well with his first railroad cases—tracking down criminals who had committed robberies and preventing others by placing operatives at likely trouble spots—that these fell off for a bit. Only a few companies hired his uniformed guards, a new approach to security. And in the first five months of its operation the agency was offered only a handful of nonrailroad cases, most of them divorce.

Joan came up with a suggestion. "Maybe you've got to go *looking* for clients."

Allan protested. "But I advertise in all the papers! What else can I do?"

She picked up a Chicago newspaper. "Here's a story about vandalism at the old French Cemetery on Lake Michigan. Chicagoans have formed a citizens' committee to do something about it."

"That's fine, but I don't see what it's got to do with me."

"Why not go to the citizens' committee and tell them you'll investigate and solve the problem?"

Allan groaned. "That's all the boys on the force need to hear—that I'm soliciting business!"

"What do you care what those loafers think?" Her tone softened. "Allan, if you solve this case—look at the attention it's been getting—you'll never have to look for another client in Chicago."

The detective visited the cemetery, where he took careful notes. He then dropped in at the library and spent some hours on research. Armed with facts, he called on the committee.

They were impressed by his ideas and his confident manner, and hired him to conduct a thorough investigation, giving him authority to use as many operatives as needed and make whatever arrests were necessary.

From his reading of past cemetery vandalism in the city, Allan was sure the suspects were either medical students, forced to steal newly buried bodies for purposes of anatomical research, since no legal provision existed for obtaining them, or young thugs who were desecrating graves out of sheer malice. It was necessary to catch only one of the vandal groups; when the other heard of its arrest, it was bound to stop its own ghoulish depredations.

He devised an alarm system that was crude but effective. Wooden stakes were driven into the ground around the entire perimeter of the cemetery except for the four entrance-exits. The stakes were strung with a light but strong twine, and small bells were hung from the twine.

Eight operatives were stationed at various points of the perimeter. If any one of them observed suspicious activity in his sector, he was to pull on the line three times. The agent nearest him would note the direction from which the tugs came, and inform his colleague by the same method to converge toward left or right. Eight men would be able to overpower and capture any vandals desecrating a grave in that part of the cemetery.

For five nights Allan Pinkerton and his men stood watch at the French Cemetery. Nothing happened. One operative saw two young men enter the grounds, but evidently the intruders' suspicions were aroused, and they fled.

For the next two nights of vigil the detective chief assigned three more men to the cemetery guard. One of them, an immigrant Irishman named Terry O'Grady, had certain misgivings about standing guard in a cemetery—he was, by his own admission, "turrible" superstitious.

"Sir," he told Allan in his thick brogue, "I must warn ye. If I was to catch sight of a ghost, I'd turn tail and run."

"Then run, Terry," the Chief told him. "Just make sure you don't get caught."

The sixth night passed without incident, but on the following night an operative in the western part of the graveyard hit pay dirt. Observing three men approaching one of the new graves, he gave his string three hard tugs. The Chief and other Pinkerton men came running, and though momentarily distracted by a piercing scream off to their right, they overpowered and handcuffed the desecrators. These proved to be medical students who confessed to several, though not all, of the grave robberies.

The group of detectives was joined by Ralph Johnson, an operative who had stood guard in the southern sector of the cemetery.

"One of you boys certainly gave Terry O'Grady a scare," he said, "running after him in that winding sheet."

Allan Pinkerton counted his men. There were ten of them. All, except O'Grady, had responded to his signal. He turned to Johnson.

"None of us here chased O'Grady, but *somebody* must have. Who could it have been?"

The men could only look blankly at one another. The Chief gave orders for the medical students to be brought to the nearest police station. Then he said to Johnson, "Come on, Ralph, we'll take a look around O'Grady's post."

His investigation satisfied the Chief that O'Grady had been the victim of a practical joke. The Irishman had been chased by something more substantial than a ghost; there were two sets of footprints leading down the exit road near which O'Grady had stood guard, and further down the road the detectives found a sheet caught on a low-hanging branch.

"It must have been one of the toughs who paid us a visit

the other night," he told Johnson. "Thought they'd throw a scare into us."

"They sure succeeded with O'Grady," grinned Johnson.

Later that night the detective dropped in at O'Grady's lodging house. He learned from the Irishman's landlady that O'Grady had hastily packed his belongings, tossed her his back rent and run from the house. Her ex-lodger, the landlady added, had been "as white as a sheet, as if the Devil himself were after him."

Terry O'Grady never returned to collect the salary due him, nor could he be located. The loss of the popular O'Grady was regretted by Allan Pinkerton and his fellow operatives, but otherwise the French Cemetery case, as it came to be known, was a complete success for the agency. Next morning the Chicago papers told of the capture of the grave robbers, and by that afternoon the waiting room at 89 Washington Street was full of prospective clients.

It was never to be empty again.

Allan Pinkerton depended on painstaking spadework and logical deduction from the facts in hand to score the major part of his successes in crime detection. But early in his career, during the summer of 1853, he demonstrated how intuition, or the hunch, can sometimes prove as valuable to the detective as a systematic investigation extending over a period of weeks or months.

One hot afternoon in July he was walking down Lake Street with a friend. He found himself staring at the back of a well-dressed man sauntering ahead of him. Why, he did not know, but something told him this man would bear watching.

He and his friend parted at the next intersection, but the detective hardly noticed. Keeping about two hundred feet behind his quarry, he followed him to the fashionable

Waverly House Hotel. There he learned the man was registered as John Harmond, of St. Louis, Missouri.

For hours the detective waited in the lobby for Harmond to reappear. He failed to, and Pinkerton returned home to a late, cold supper. He brought with him some purchases of clothing he had made along the way.

At 5:00 A.M. the next morning a short but burly workman, wielding a mortar hoe, was at work on a bed of mortar near the Waverly House carriage drive. He wore stained work clothes and an old felt hat; near him stood a lunch pail.

The suspect appeared at 5:30, carrying a suitcase, and set off for the Michigan Central Railroad Station, a few blocks away. The workman put down his hoe and followed.

Harmond bought a ticket for the Detroit Special, due to leave in thirty minutes. As he left the station and sauntered down toward the lake, the shabby workman put down the newspaper he had been reading and followed him, keeping his distance. At the lakefront he hunkered down behind a trash can.

Harmond approached within a few feet of the water. Then, after looking carefully around, he knelt down and started digging in the sand.

The workman saw him lift a metal box from its hiding place. Harmond opened it. There was a brief sparkle, as of precious stones. Harmond slipped the contents of the box into his pocket, then tossed the box far out into the lake.

When Harmond entered the day coach to Detroit, there was only one vacant seat. It was next to a grimy workman, but the well-dressed traveler, evidently no snob, sat down beside him. He opened his newspaper and began to read. There were five minutes till the train was due to leave.

Suddenly the workman took a pair of handcuffs from his pocket. "Harmond," he snapped, "you're under arrest," and moved to lock the cuffs on the wrists of his companion.

Harmond jumped to his feet. The shabby figure grappled with him, and Harmond shouted. "Help! This madman's trying to steal my wallet!"

A few venturesome passengers left their seats to observe the commotion, but no one took sides. Harmond was a powerful man, and his assailant was getting the worst of the fight when the conductor pushed his way down the aisle.

He separated the two men. "Stop this," he ordered, "or I'll call the police."

"I am the police," Allan said, breathing heavily. "I'm arresting this man for robbery."

A laugh went up from the onlookers, and seeing the doubtful look on the conductor's face as he examined this shabby workingman who claimed to be the law, Harmond took advantage of both.

"Police!" he sneered. "The man's a thief. Look at his clothes! Let him prove he isn't!"

"Where's your identification?" the conductor asked.

As Allan showed him his credentials the train whistle sounded in warning. The conductor hailed a passing brakeman, and together the two men took Harmond, protesting loudly, to the stationmaster's office. The train left without him.

A short time later Harmond was behind bars at the police station. An impressive heap of rings, jeweled pins and gold watches—all taken from his pockets—lay on the sergeant's desk, together with over a thousand dollars in cash.

Allan Pinkerton, still in his workman's clothes, returned to Waverly House. He found the place in an uproar. Guests, some of them in night clothes, were besieging the manager with shouted demands that he call the police, that he search the hotel for their stolen valuables.

The doorman tried to prevent the shabbily dressed workingman from entering the lobby. "Look here," he snapped, "where do you think *you're* going?"

Pinkerton brushed past him and, vaulting to the top of the main desk, raised a hand for silence.

"I'm Allan Pinkerton, a detective," he told the gaping crowd. "I've caught the man who stole your jewelry, money and watches. You can pick them up at State Street station."

In complete silence he jumped to the floor, walked across the lobby and out the door.

The jewels Harmond had buried in the sand by Lake Michigan were later discovered to have been stolen from a Toledo, Ohio, jeweler. After trial Harmond was sentenced to a long term at Illinois Penitentiary. Allan Pinkerton signed an agreement with Waverly House whereby his agency provided the hotel with round-the-clock protection against guests of John Harmond's particular talents.

The Harmond case resulted in the first of many agreements to be reached between Pinkerton's National and Chicago hotels. The business it brought to the agency, along with some new railroad and corporation accounts, enabled the detective chief to enlarge his full-time roster of employees considerably. It also had another effect: the creation of a special wardrobe room at the Washington Street office where wigs and disguises of almost any description were made available to operatives who might find them useful in their work.

In his work for the railroads the Chief traveled extensively through the states bordering the Mason-Dixon Line, and this gave him an excellent opportunity to carry on his activities in behalf of the Underground Railroad. In the years 1853–1859 he was instrumental in passing over a hundred Negro families through Underground stations to freedom in Canada and the North. The house on Adams Street often sheltered fugitive slaves liberated by Abolitionist John Brown on one of his plantation raids. If Joan Pinkerton objected to the drain this made on the family finances, she never said so. Her only advice to her husband was to be careful. Proslavers had sworn to string up any interfering Abolitionists found in their midst.

During the summer of 1859, while traveling through Tennessee on combined railroad and Underground Railroad business, Allan Pinkerton stopped in the town of Columbia.

The president of the local bank, a man named Lowrey, called on the detective with a strange case. The crime, involving murder, had been committed over a year ago. Jackson Carter, a cashier at the bank, had worked late one evening. The following morning he was found dead, lying near his desk with his head crushed in. The lock of the rear door had been forced, establishing the murderer's method of entry.

Lowrey's suspicions had come to rest on one man in town, John Slocum. Slocum had been a close friend of Carter's, yet when the bank president, after discovering the body, had asked him to look at it, Slocum refused, begging off with the excuse that his nerves couldn't take so terrible a sight. Then Lowrey had noticed some burned papers in the bank's furnace grate. Among them was a charred scrap that appeared to be an IOU for a large sum from Slocum to Carter.

"That's fairly good circumstantial evidence," commented the detective. "Good enough to get Slocum taken in for questioning."

Lowrey shook his head. "Slocum's highly thought of in this town, and some of his best friends are my depositors. I'd lose them if I ever suggested such a thing on present evidence."

Allan Pinkerton pondered for a moment. "How has Slocum been acting in recent months? Pretty normally?"

"No, and that's another thing. He hardly sticks his nose

out of the door any more, and folks say he's become a regular recluse."

"Well, if he won't come to us, we'll have to go to him."

The banker was doubtful. "How are you going to manage that? Slocum won't even let tradesmen into the house. It's gotten so he can't keep his help. Three housekeepers have walked out on him in the last few months."

"Servants," the detective muttered thoughtfully. "Maybe that's the answer. It could be the answer for Jock and Mary Littleton."

"Who are these Littletons?"

"Before I answer that question, Mr. Lowrey, I'll have to ask one of my own. What are your feelings on the slavery question?"

"I incline toward Abolition, but I wouldn't want to see the states go to war over it."

Pinkerton nodded. "That's good enough. Mr. Lowrey, Jock and Mary Littleton are escaped slaves, and fine people. At the moment they're holed up in an Underground station in Huntsville, Alabama. If I could bring them here, to take over Slocum's household, it would help a great deal in ultimately getting them over the line. They could also function as our undercover operators in bringing Slocum to justice."

"I won't stand in your way. But may I ask how this Negro couple can help get Slocum for us? By this time he's had more than enough time to destroy any papers that connect him with Jackson Carter."

"True," nodded the detective. "But you're forgetting Slocum's state of mind. It's showing signs of heavy strain. We can strain it further, to the point of breakdown. The criminal must always confess his crime, which haunts him continually; the burden of concealment becomes, finally, too heavy to bear alone. It must find a voice, and the detective has only to wait for a weak moment to force the secret from him."

"I see what you're driving at. How soon can you get your colored couple to Columbia?"

"As soon as you can get them hired."

"That shouldn't take long. Slocum's desperate for help, and he's wary of the local people. I won't have any trouble talking him into taking the Littletons on. Will you handle the case personally, Mr. Pinkerton, or are you sending someone down to take over?"

"You'll have Timothy Webster, my best man. But I'll be in Columbia from time to time."

"Webster? Haven't heard of him."

"You will. Someday Timothy Webster—ex-actor, ex-preacher, ex-soldier of fortune—is going to be the most famous detective in the United States."

"That's quite a tall order," Lowrey said, "when the fellow has you to reckon with as competition."

"Oh, I'm not interested in fame, Mr. Lowrey," grinned the detective. "The more anonymous I manage to stay, the better."

Timothy Webster, a large, florid man in his late thirties, with a bay window and a penchant for elegant dress, arrived in Columbia a few days after Jock and Mary Littleton had been hired by John Slocum as butler and cook-housemaid. He conferred with the banker and the Negro couple, and then went to work.

Among the murdered man's effects Webster found a half-empty bottle of a strong cologne which the cashier had used profusely. His first move was to instruct the Littletons to scatter drops of this scent over Slocum's linen, handkerchiefs and towels. It was Allan Pinkerton's suggestion that Webster also ask the couple to sprinkle crimson dye about the Slocum household. "Perhaps on the white flowers in the garden," he wrote his operative in Columbia, "perhaps on the bedsheets and pillowcases. The initials 'J. C.' might also be traced in this same bloodlike dye on various objects, but not so clearly as to make Slocum wonder if a ghost would have written in so legible a hand."

These methods proved immediately successful. The Littletons reported to Webster at his command post at the Columbia Hotel that Slocum had now moved to the library, where he took his meals and slept behind locked doors. His nerves were in a terrible state.

Banker Lowrey had some objections to the way things were going. He was afraid that Webster would drive Slocum insane or that Slocum would try to cheat justice by committing suicide.

Webster disagreed. "He can't take much more of this punishment, you're right there. But the next thing he'll do is make a run for it, away from Columbia, and I'll be right behind him."

On the night Allan Pinkerton returned to Columbia to resume direction of the Slocum case, Webster played his trump card. In the basement of the Slocum house Jock Littleton installed a speaking tube which led to the library where his employer spent his days and nights behind locked doors. Starting at midnight, this speaking tube emitted, at regular intervals, a series of hollow, terrifying groans.

At dawn the next morning Timothy Webster roused the Chief. "It's happened, boss. Littleton just came by to say Slocum's all packed and ready to catch the five forty-five to Nashville."

Pinkerton rubbed his eyes and asked, "What time is it now?"

"Ten past five."

"Just enough time to catch the train, if we hurry. Be sure to bring along that bottle of Carter's cologne."

The two detectives swung aboard the Nashville Special as it pulled out of the Columbia station.

Suddenly Webster struck his forehead with a balled fist and groaned. "Boss, we're in trouble. With Slocum shut up in that house all the time, I was never able to see what he looks like. And there are at least fifty men on this train."

"Don't worry. We'll ask the conductor who got on at Columbia."

Three men were pointed out to the detectives. One was too young to be Slocum. The others, both middle-aged men who answered his general description, sat together talking.

Pinkerton and Webster took a vacant seat a few rows behind them.

"Let's have the cologne," Pinkerton whispered. Taking out his handkerchief, he sprinkled it liberally with the strong-smelling scent.

"I'll walk past those two, flourishing this handkerchief," he told Webster. "Whichever one is unduly disturbed is the man we're after."

The stratagem worked. As Pinkerton, pretending to blow his nose, passed the two men, the taller of the two paled, muttered something and got to his feet. He fairly flew past the detective to the smoker beyond. Casting a stricken look about him, he parted the curtains and stepped inside.

Webster joined the Chief outside the smoker. "What's next?" he asked.

"I'm going to follow Slocum inside. If he comes rushing out, grab him. He might try to jump off the train."

In the smoker Slocum sat near the window he had raised, breathing heavily and with his cravat undone. Allan Pinkerton, the scented handkerchief in his breast pocket, took a seat opposite him. Then, after a moment, he moved to one of the wash basins only a few feet from his quarry and began soaping his hands.

"Train's making good time," he commented to Slocum, and shutting off the tap, turned to smile at him.

Slocum stared at the stranger, his mouth agape. There was naked terror in his eyes. In the small, almost airless smoker, the smell of Jackson Carter's scent was overpowering.

"What's the matter, sir?" the detective asked quietly. "Is there something wrong?"

With an anguished cry Slocum rushed from the smoker. Allan Pinkerton threw down his towel and followed. But he was seconds too late. Outside the curtained doorway Slocum had collided with Webster and knocked him off his feet. Now he stood on the vestibule platform, poised to jump.

"Slocum, don't!" Allan shouted, and leaped for the emergency cord.

As he pulled on it, Slocum leaped from the fast-moving train.

The detectives, accompanied by two trainmen, found him at the bottom of a gully, fatally injured but still conscious.

Allan Pinkerton didn't fight the pity he felt, but he had a job to do. Slocum was a murderer, and justice demanded that he confess his crime before he died.

"You don't have too long," he told him. "Isn't there something on your conscience?"

"Yes," Slocum whispered, as the witnesses pressed forward to hear. "A man named Jackson Carter . . . I killed him . . . for a debt I . . . couldn't pay. I'm sorry. . . . Funny . . . he wore a scent . . . just like yours." His voice failed him, and his head dropped to one side.

Back in Columbia affidavits of Slocum's confession signed by the trainmen were filed officially, and the case closed.

Banker Lowrey was grateful. But he had bad news for Allan Pinkerton. He had just received a wire from a leading Abolitionist. It read: "John Brown's raid at Harper's Ferry to seize federal arms a tragic failure. At this moment Brown and his men besieged by overwhelming U. S. Marine forces under command of Colonel Robert E. Lee."

5 The Plot to Kill Abraham Lincoln

ALLAN PINKERTON WAS TOO DEDICATED A FOE OF SLAVERY NOT to consider doing what he could to free John Brown, whether or not northern officials approved. He wired over thirty agents, in various southern states, to leave their present assignments and meet with him in Charlestown, where Brown had been taken and jailed.

He ignored his clients' chorus of indignant complaints. Should they wish to tear up their agency contracts, he told them, they were free to do so. "Present business of the utmost importance requires the presence of my agents elsewhere at the moment," he wrote them, and that was all he wrote. Had he been facing bankruptcy, the Chief would still have gone to Charlestown to plot John Brown's escape. Third a businessman, and second a policeman, he was first a man of ideals.

Yet he was a realist, too. After a week in Charlestown he concluded there was simply no way of penetrating the massive, well-guarded prison without additional loss of life. More blood spilled in Virginia in the Abolitionist cause would set it back for years. His Abolitionist friends and associates listened, and reluctantly agreed.

On December 2, 1859, John Brown was taken from his cell and hung for treason. Charlestown emptied of Abolitionists. Those Pinkerton agents not discharged by clients for leaving their posts returned to work, and the Chief went home to Chicago.

Lincoln's election to the Presidency in November of the next year pleased Allan Pinkerton greatly. He knew and admired Abraham Lincoln from the days when he was investigating robberies for the Illinois Central Railroad, which the new President had served as counsel. Lincoln had promised to prevent the extension of slavery, and declared that the government could not endure "half slave and half free." This was real Abolitionism for you!

Troubles between North and South took a turn that involved the agency directly. Samuel Felton, president of the Philadelphia, Wilmington and Baltimore Railroad, learned that Maryland Secessionists were plotting to cut Washington off from the northern states by destroying the railroad's ferryboats at Havre de Grace and a number of its bridges in Delaware. Allan Pinkerton was called in to deal with the threat.

After investigation in several Maryland and Delaware cities, he concluded that the Maryland hotheads were, at least for the moment, more talk than action. But it was undeniable that feeling in the southern state was running high against the government. In Baltimore there was a possibility of armed insurrection. The majority of city officials, the wealthier classes and the mob element were all in favor of an armed uprising. There were rumors that Marshal George P. Kane openly advocated an insurrection on the twenty-fourth of February, the day President-elect Lincoln was due to pass through the city on his way to Washington for the inauguration. If that happened, Philadelphia railroad property, known to be Yankee owned, would be seriously threatened, not to mention the probability of injury to the President.

Allan Pinkerton called on the colonel of the army garrison and told him his fears. He was told in turn that the army was in firm control of Baltimore and that any real trouble was unlikely.

"I beg to disagree," said the detective. "If you were to listen to the violent, seditious talk at places like Guy's Restaurant and Barnum's Hotel, you might form a different opinion."

"I don't have time to sit in Guy's and glut myself on terrapin," the colonel replied stiffly. "Evidently you, sir, do." He got to his feet, signifying that the interview was over.

The detective wired Norman Judd, a friend and fellow Chicagoan now with the President's party in Springfield, Illinois, about the current unrest in Baltimore. Either Judd failed to receive the wire or he considered the detective's anxiety unwarranted. In any case, he failed to reply.

Allan Pinkerton rented suitable headquarters in Baltimore —a house on South Street whose advantage was that it had a number of entrances and exits. There he received the reports of his agents, most of them stationed at various points along the Philadelphia Railroad right-of-way between Baltimore and the Susquehanna Ferry. Among these agents working in and around Baltimore were Timothy Webster, the dapper Harry Davies and Mrs. Kate Warne, the agency's first woman operative. Kate was later to rise to the rank of superintendent of Pinkerton's National "female department." Now the attractive young woman wore the Secessionist's black and white cockade, and had already proved herself by penetrating Baltimore's most hotly rebellious circles. Her reports were models of intelligence and precision and convinced Allan Pinkerton that in some instances women detectives were as reliable as men.

It was Webster and Davies who, in the last weeks of January, contributed the most valuable undercover work. Webster managed to join a volunteer troop of cavalry secretly pledged to join Baltimoreans when they rose up against the

Yankee tyrant. Davies, operating under the name of Joseph Howard of New Orleans and spending freely in Baltimore's more elegant saloons, was working for an invitation to join the select Palmetto Guards, another volunteer group dedicated to upholding southern rights. He was already friendly with Marshal Kane.

Early in the morning of February 3, Timothy Webster woke the Chief with dreadful news. Plans for the Baltimore uprising had now been broadened to include a conspiracy to seize Washington after assassinating President-elect Lincoln as he passed through the city. Webster had overheard officers of the volunteer troop discussing the assassination with representatives of the Palmetto Guards. The two groups planned to work closely together to guarantee success of the Guards' plans.

Horrified, Pinkerton sent immediately to Barnum's Hotel for Davies, and told him Webster's news. "You've got to work faster now, Harry, on joining the Palmettos and becoming a member of their inside circle. We have only a few weeks to learn their plans in detail."

Davies nodded, and Webster asked his Chief, "Hadn't you better warn President Lincoln?"

Pinkerton shook his head. "The President won't be convinced without all the facts before him. I can't go to him without them, and so far Norman Judd's been no help."

Davies' diatribes against "that Black Republican Lincoln," and his loud and oft-repeated opinion that the South would be better off with Vice President Andrew Johnson at the helm, had their desired effect. With Marshal Kane and others vouching for him, he was sworn in as a Palmetto Guard and ordered to attend a meeting of "vast importance" where the "deed of the century" was to be discussed.

Davies reported this meeting in detail at the house on South Street. More than thirty men had been present, among them members of Webster's cavalry troop. After a series of inflammatory speeches, Marshal Kane, the presiding officer, came to the point: the group was here to choose the assassins of Abraham Lincoln. The deed was to be accomplished outside Baltimore's Calvert Street Station, after the President left his special train. A gang of toughs would start a fight which would be a pretext for most of the police to leave Lincoln's side. Then, as the crowd closed in around the Presidential party, pushing and jostling, creating a noisy confusion, the assassin would pull his pistol from his pocket and fire. The plan was foolproof; southern agents would be sent to all cities along the President's route to watch the movements of Lincoln's party, and be ready to wire, in cipher, to Baltimore any change of route or delay. The assassin would make his escape via carriage and chartered Chesapeake Bay steamer.

Secret ballots would be drawn to choose the President's killer. One ballot would be red, the others white. The man who drew the red ballot would have the privilege and honor of striking "the blow for southern freedom that would forever echo down the corridors of time."

The lights were dimmed, and one by one the men drew their ballots. Then the lights went up again. Davies saw that he had chosen a white ballot. But from the looks on the faces of his fellow conspirators, he was certain that more than one red ballot had been drawn. At least seven men were visibly pale or trembling.

"Seven men," Allan Pinkerton said, when Davies had finished his story. "Seven men with cocked pistols, sworn to kill Lincoln. The President will *have* to believe me. Harry, write your report in detail. The Presidential party arrives in Philadelphia tomorrow morning. I'll leave for there tonight."

Philadelphia, in anticipation of the President's arrival, was hung with flags and bunting. The city's air of joyful hospitality contrasted sharply with Baltimore's atmosphere of hysterical hostility. As the President's carriage passed through crowds of cheering thousands on its route from the station to the Continental Hotel, a Pinkerton agent thrust his way through the police cordon and handed one of the Presidential party a folded slip of paper. Its recipient was Norman Judd. The message read: "A matter of life and death. St. Louis Hotel. Ask for J. H. Hutchinson."

After the Presidential party had arrived at the Continental Hotel, Judd hastened to the St. Louis. There he knocked on a door which was answered by a powerfully built man of forty-one with sharp eyes and a grim expression.

"Allan!" Judd exclaimed. "What are you doing in Philadelphia? Does it have anything to do with that wire of yours? What's all this hocus-pocus?"

"Come in, Norman, and I'll explain."

As Judd came into the room Samuel Felton, president of the Philadelphia Railroad, got to his feet. Before Felton, on a table, were several folders of evidence, including Harry Davies' report.

An hour later a carriage deposited the three men at the Continental Hotel. The corridors were jammed, and they had to force their way through to the suite of John Nicolay, the President's secretary.

Nicolay agreed to bring President Lincoln to Judd's room, and the three men waited there for him. Lincoln arrived with Nicolay a few minutes later. As the tall, gaunt man strode into the room, Allan Pinkerton experienced an almost physical shock, so great was the effect of his magnetism, his presence.

Lincoln greeted his visitors cordially, and then Allan Pinkerton explained the reason for what might appear to be an unwarranted intrusion. "Mr. President, we have proof that there exists a plot to assassinate you on your way to Baltimore the day after tomorrow."

It was plain the President was less than convinced. "Thank you, Mr. Pinkerton," he said drily. "Have you brought your proof with you?"

"I have, sir," the detective said, and produced, piece by piece, the contents of the folders. Lincoln studied each carefully, questioning the detective minutely after reading each one. It was as if he were a lawyer cross-examining a witness hostile to his client. He seemed especially interested in Harry Davies' report of the Palmetto Guards meeting.

The doubtful manner seemed to pass. He looked at Nicolay and said, almost whispering the words, "Why do they want to kill me?"

"Sir," Pinkerton broke in to answer, "it would be impossible for a man of your mind and temperament to understand how fanatical the opposition is to you in and around Baltimore. The extremist elements expect you to destroy them, either by using force, which they aren't prepared to meet at the moment, or by conciliation, which would just as effectively destroy the firebrands and their influence by cutting the ground from under their feet."

Lincoln smiled. "Mr. Pinkerton, you might think like a detective, but you talk like a politician, a good one. Now may I ask what you propose to do about this conspiracy?"

"We propose to take you directly to Washington tonight, thus bypassing your enemies. It will require cancellation of your program for tomorrow in Philadelphia and Harrisburg."

The President turned to Nicolay. "John, do you agree with Mr. Pinkerton?"

Nicolay nodded. "I do. Caution would seem to rule out any other course of action."

Lincoln thought a moment. Then he said, "Gentlemen, I appreciate the work you have done, and your suggestions.

But I cannot accept them completely. I have promised to raise the flag over Independence Hall tomorrow morning and to dine, in Harrisburg, with the governor. At whatever cost, these two promises I must fulfill. Thereafter I am ready to listen to your plans."

He rose, and shook hands all around, with special warmth in his clasp for Allan Pinkerton. Then, preceding Nicolay, he left the room.

Abraham Lincoln slept badly that night. Allan Pinkerton didn't sleep at all, nor did the men he had asked to confer with him on plans to bring the President safely from Harrisburg to Washington. These, in addition to Judd and Felton, were G. C. Franciscus, general manager of the Pennsylvania Railroad, and E. S. Sanford, representing the American Telegraph Company.

After raising the flag over Independence Hall, the President proceeded by carriage to the special train which would take him to Harrisburg, the state capital. Five minutes before the train was due to leave, one of Lincoln's aides came rushing up with an urgent dispatch from Washington.

The dispatch consisted of letters from William H. Seward, Secretary of State, and General Winfield Scott, Commander-in-Chief of the Army. Both warned the President about passing through Baltimore at the possible cost of his life. Seward and Scott had received their information via northern investigators assigned to Baltimore to look into rumors that the southern city was seething with malcontents whose hostility was potentially explosive. These investigators had arrived at the same conclusions as Pinkerton and his men, although they had failed to uncover a definite plot for assassination.

Lincoln turned to Judd, sitting beside him in the parlor car. "After this, I do not doubt the reality of the danger." To Allan Pinkerton he said, "Proceed with your plans."

"Mr. President," answered the detective, "I will answer with my life for your safe conduct to Washington."

Allan Pinkerton had provided for every possible contingency that could occur in Harrisburg. Southern spies were there watching the President's every move. If they learned that Lincoln had left Harrisburg at a time different from what his schedule called for, they would wire an immediate alarm to the conspirators in Baltimore. If the conspirators had reason to suspect that Lincoln and his party were on to their game, the odds were good they would change their plans and attempt to dispatch him elsewhere and by other means. There lay the chief danger, for the President's protectors were at a disadvantage with an attack that might come at any time, from any quarter.

The train left the station for Harrisburg with two Pinkerton operatives aboard, thoroughly briefed and heavily armed. The detective chief then returned to the St. Louis Hotel to wait for any new communications from Webster and Davies, still in Baltimore, or from still another source.

He had arranged with the American Telegraph Company to have all messages over their wires from Harrisburg intercepted in the Philadelphia office. Among these might be coded communications from southern spies to headquarters in Baltimore. There was one exception: messages addressed to J. H. Hutchinson, Allan Pinkerton himself.

Aside from American Telegraph, there was only one other method of communication between Harrisburg and Baltimore. This was over the telegraph line of the Northern Central Railroad. With Samuel Felton's help, arrangements were made to put the line out of order for a period of twenty-four hours.

In Harrisburg the Presidential banquet began at five o'clock. At six, President Lincoln slipped away from the table with the excuse that he was suffering from a slight headache.

But instead of returning to his room upstairs at the hotel, he met Judd, the Pinkertons and Governor Curtin of Pennsylvania at a side entrance of the hotel.

A carriage was waiting there. Governor Curtin was last to get in. For the benefit of any southern agents who might have recognized the President, Curtin loudly ordered the driver to take the party to the executive mansion.

The carriage, its shade drawn, avoided the crowds at the front of the hotel and headed, not for the executive mansion, but for a railroad crossing at the outskirts of the city.

At the crossing waited the fast locomotive and darkened passenger coach that Allan Pinkerton had arranged for. The President, wearing a traveling shawl over his overcoat, went aboard, accompanied by two Pinkertons and three members of his party.

The famous secret journey of February 22 from Harrisburg to Washington had begun.

The President's car sped eastward to Downington, Pennsylvania, where it took on water. The passengers disembarked for refreshments, except for Lincoln, to whom a cup of tea and a roll were brought. From Downington the car continued on to the station at West Philadelphia.

The first man to jump aboard there was Allan Pinkerton. President Lincoln greeted him with a smile. "Mr. Pinkerton," he said, "you look rather fatigued. I understand you have been waiting all day for a message from a certain elusive gentleman named Hutchinson."

The detective pretended surprise. "Now why should I do that, sir? I never even met the man, though he does seem worth knowing."

The President and his party transferred to a carriage which took them, by a roundabout route, to the Philadelphia Railroad Station on Carpenter Street. They all alighted in the shadow of a high fence, and waited while Allan Pinkerton took a quick look around. Then he led them through the yards to the Washington train. There was a scattering of travelers on the platform. As the President approached the last sleeping car, Kate Warne stepped forward and said, warmly, "Brother William, you're indeed a sight for a loving sister's eyes!"

The tall "brother" handed his attractive "sister" into the train, and the family party—so it had been represented to the conductor—followed after. One of the party, a short, powerfully built man, emerged on the rear platform and, looking about him at the typical station bustle, casually lit a cigar.

The Washington-bound train left the station at 10:55. Allan Pinkerton did not leave the rear platform, not even as the miles clicked away and the night grew cold. Around midnight Kate Warne brought him a cup of tea.

The train stopped at Perryville, Timothy Webster's area of operation and the first Secessionist stronghold through which the train would have to pass. As yardmen prepared to ferry the train across the Susquehanna River, Allan Pinkerton peered into the blackness, hoping to see two flashes of lantern light.

The bull's eye flashes came from near the ferry slip, and the detective expelled his breath in a satisfied sigh. Thank the Lord for Timothy Webster and his signal, which meant not only that all was well, but that the operative had successfully stationed other Pinkertons and railroad workers along the route from Perryville to Baltimore against the possibility of a blown bridge or a destroyed trestle. At every major junction he could expect to catch a similar signal.

The cars were ferried across the river and rejoined to their locomotive on the opposite shore. The journey was resumed, and from every junction along the way came the reassuring lantern flashes.

The train stopped in Baltimore Station at 3:30 A.M. The platform was deserted, and no suspicious figures lurked in the shadows as the sleeping cars were uncoupled for their horse-drawn trip through Baltimore streets to the station of the Washington line.

Once there the passengers had a tedious wait. A connecting train due from Chicago was almost two hours overdue. To help pass the time, the detective joined the President in his compartment, where he was chatting with Kate Warne.

"Did you anticipate this delay, too, Mr. Pinkerton?" the President asked him cheerfully. "If you say no, I'll be disappointed."

"Sorry to disappoint you, sir, but I can't predict the future —at least not that well."

"I've been telling Mr. Lincoln about your precautions along the route," Kate Warne said, "and he thinks you're capable of miracles."

The detective grinned. "If I were capable of miracles, Mr. President, we'd already be in Washington."

From time to time the waiting northerners could hear snatches of song from the station waiting room. People were singing rebel songs, "My Maryland" and "Dixie."

"Such impressive songs," the President commented sadly, "and sung with such moving fervor."

"Oh, there are many patriots in Baltimore," Kate Warne said drily, and both men laughed.

The train finally left Baltimore, and it was with profound relief that Allan Pinkerton resumed his place on the rear platform. He could afford to relax now. The President was safe, and the mission to protect him, accomplished. If he achieved nothing else in his lifetime, these last few hours had been enough to justify his existence.

He couldn't help feeling a certain pride. He had perhaps saved the President's life; beyond a doubt, he had sat across from Abraham Lincoln and made light conversation with the sixteenth President of the United States. The Scots errand boy, the Chartist fugitive, the penniless immigrant, had come a long way in the land of his adoption.

The train pulled into Washington Station at five minutes after six in the morning. Surrounded by Pinkerton men, the President, exhausted from sleeplessness and the strain of his journey, moved slowly toward the exit. A corner of his traveling shawl dragged along the ground, and Allan Pinkerton bent forward and picked it up.

The station was fairly crowded, and several people recognized the President, whose tall figure dwarfed his companions. A congressman stopped to greet Lincoln, expressing surprise that he was back so soon from Baltimore.

"Please!" Allan Pinkerton interrupted him. "No talking here!"

The congressman wheeled around in great affront. "And who might you be, sir?" he inquired contemptuously. "Your face is unfamiliar to me."

"That's Allan Pinkerton," the President said. "His face won't be unfamiliar to you very long."

Seward and Scott were waiting for Lincoln in a closed carriage, which left immediately for the Willard Hotel. The Pinkertons followed in a cab. A short time later, Allan Pinkerton was called to the Presidential suite to receive Lincoln's official thanks.

"Mr. Pinkerton," the President added, "such talents as yours should be used. You will be hearing from me."

"I am delighted, sir. Now about the plotters—do you wish their arrest?"

The President shook his head. "I have no desire to make martyrs out of madmen and cowards."

Allan Pinkerton returned to Baltimore and the house on South Street. Though desperate for sleep, he was determined to stay awake until Webster and Davies returned with their final reports.

They showed up a few hours later. The plotters, they said, had known of Lincoln's arrival in Washington by eight o'clock that morning, and fled Baltimore in mingled rage and panic. Marshal Kane had left for Richmond with his family. All Baltimore was convinced that hundreds of military spies and Yankee secret police swarmed over the city.

Davies was adding a number of details when Timothy Webster nudged him in the ribs. "Stop, Harry. Can't you see the Chief's not with you? He's fallen fast asleep!"

Returning to his Chicago office, Pinkerton found the waiting room jammed with reporters. The detective denied that he was responsible for foiling the Baltimore plotters. He insisted that at least half a dozen of his operatives, Timothy Webster chief among them, deserved the credit for saving Abraham Lincoln's life.

6 "Major Allen" Snares a Spy

Charleston gunners shelled Fort Sumter on April 12, 1861, beginning the Civil War. Three days later President Lincoln issued a call for seventy-five thousand volunteers. On April 19 the Sixth Massachusetts Infantry Regiment, crossing Baltimore on its way to the Washington station, had to resort to the bayonet in order to fight off an enraged mob screaming "Secession!" and "Death to the Union!" The predictions of anti-Union riots in Baltimore made by Allan Pinkerton less than two months before had come to pass in a way that shocked the nation.

Less than twenty-four hours later, seven bridges in Pennsylvania and Maryland, which were essential to railroad communications between Washington and New York, were either blown up or destroyed by fire. Telegraph wires were cut. To protect the isolated government Lincoln had only a few battalions of troops.

The immediate outlook was none too bright. The Federal army numbered only seventeen thousand. Rebel spies and Secessionist agitators swarmed in northern cities. President Buchanan had done nothing to cope with them, leaving this problem, and a host of others, to his Republican successor.

A number of prominent Chicagoans had important messages for the President. They approached Allan Pinkerton

79

for a courier who could get through to Washington, and he supplied Timothy Webster.

Carrying dispatches sewn into his waistcoat lining by Kate Warne, Webster arrived in Philadelphia. From there he went on to Perryman, Maryland, for a reunion with his comrades of the cavalry troop. They were glad to provide so zealous a fellow rebel with a military pass which took him through southern pickets into Washington.

Secretary Nicolay hurried the dispatches to President Lincoln. Lincoln gave Webster his personal thanks, along with two messages to be sent by telegraph as soon as the detective reached a station in operation outside the capital city. One message was to General George B. McClellan, in Columbus, Ohio; the other to Allan Pinkerton, asking that he come to Washington as soon as possible to discuss the possibility of organizing a Federal secret service.

The President asked Webster how he planned to carry the messages, and the dapper detective showed him a cane which unscrewed into two hollow cylinders.

"If you would like one of these for yourself, Mr. President," said Webster, "I can have it sent from Philadelphia."

Lincoln laughed. "I'm just a country boy, Mr. Webster. On the day I can swing so elegant a cane without looking foolish, New York State will secede from the Union."

When he received Webster's message, Allan Pinkerton departed by train for Washington, leaving word at his Chicago office for Webster to wait for him in Pittsburgh. In the capital he conferred with Lincoln and the cabinet on the question of organizing a secret service department. Some cabinet members, he discovered to his surprise and concern, were less convinced than he about the necessity for such an organization.

"Gentlemen," he told them earnestly, "southern spies are invading the North like locusts. They have a big head start already. We ourselves must put hundreds of operatives into the field to learn the South's military plans. And there is also the matter of investigating traitors in our midst; Washington is particularly vulnerable in this matter."

Salmon P. Chase, Secretary of the Treasury, cleared his throat pompously. "Sir, I wish you could prove your allegations. The fact remains that as yet we have not caught a single important southern agent."

"And why?" asked the detective. "Because we have no one to catch them with!"

The conference adjourned with little or nothing accomplished. Lincoln, who seemed preoccupied with weightier matters, thanked the detective for coming to the capital at his own expense. He added that it was probably too soon to put a secret service into operation; the new administration was in too great a state of confusion. However, he would be in touch with Mr. Pinkerton later on.

At his Washington hotel the detective found a wire forwarded from Chicago. It read: "Have heard of your achievement in protecting the President and would appreciate your coming to see me in Columbus. Observe caution. If you telegraph me, be sure to use only your first name. Let no one know your plans."

It was signed "George B. McClellan, Major General Commanding, Ohio Volunteers."

The detective had heard of George McClellan, a West Point graduate, who had fought with distinction in the Mexican War at Chapultepec and Monterey. Some people already spoke of him as Lincoln's next chief of staff, despite Winfield Scott's greater fame and rank.

Pinkerton left Washington for Philadelphia, and there boarded the next train for Pittsburgh, where he had some business.

He was in time to save Timothy Webster from possible lynching as a southern spy.

Webster, quietly sipping a drink in the bar of his hotel, had happened to attract the attention of a superpatriot who was denouncing the President and General Scott for failing to sack and destroy Baltimore.

"Hey, you!" the patriot bellowed at Webster, "What's your opinion?"

"I doubt if every person in Baltimore is a rebel hothead," replied Webster reasonably.

"Oh, you do, do you?" sneered the patriot. "You a pro-slaver yourself?"

Webster shook his head patiently. "I come from Princeton, New Jersey."

"Is that right?" the zealot persisted. "Well, you sure do dress like a fancy dan rebel." His eyes narrowed. "And what about all those telegrams you've been getting? Who are they from—Jeff Davis?"

"That, sir," Webster answered mildly, "is my business."

The fanatic reddened with anger. "You're a confounded spy!" he burst out suddenly.

There was an ugly mutter in the crowded room, and the detective realized that in the eyes of these men he had become, to all intents and purposes, exactly what this fool accused him of being.

From the back someone yelled, "Let's lynch him!"

A group of angry men surged forward. Webster backed away, drawing his revolver. One of the group shouted: "Watch out! The traitor's got a pistol!"

"You're talking nonsense," Webster said calmly. "None of you can prove a single thing you've said. I'm warning you— the first man to attack me is going to regret it."

Heads turned as someone pushed his way through the

crowd. Webster smiled and heaved a sigh of relief. It was Allan Pinkerton.

The stocky detective exuded authority. So did the revolver he held in his hand. "Gentlemen," he said, nodding toward Webster, "you're doing this man a great injustice. He's no traitor, but loyal to the core."

"Yes, but to what side?" demanded the zealot craftily.

"Yes, make him prove he's for the Union!" another man shouted.

"Let's bring him to the mayor," a would-be lyncher put in, and there was a yell of approval.

Allan Pinkerton shrugged. The mayor of Pittsburgh would never permit a lynching in his city.

Outside the hotel the City Hall–bound crowd encountered Pittsburgh's chief of police, called to investigate the disturbance. He knew Allan Pinkerton, and was willing to accept his word on Webster.

The crowd dispersed with reluctance. The police chief invited the detectives to headquarters for a cup of coffee.

There they learned this was not the first such incident to happen in Pittsburgh. Only a week ago mobs had beaten three perfectly innocent people and injured a dozen more. "I hear in other parts of the country it's even worse," the police chief said. "They hung a man in Wilmington."

Timothy Webster shuddered, and whispered to his boss. "You know, Chief, I'd feel a lot safer spying in the South!"

In Columbus Allan Pinkerton conferred with McClellan. The General was short, handsome and dynamic with piercing light blue eyes. To the detective he seemed one of the most impressive men he had ever met—also one of the most ambitious. McClellan made no secret of the fact that he saw himself as a man of destiny and meant to replace doddering old Winfield Scott as chief of staff of the Union armies. Yet so

charming and enthusiastic was McClellan that one didn't
mind his lack of modesty.

Allan Pinkerton jokingly asked the General if he didn't
expect some competition from Sam Grant of Missouri. In
Washington he had heard some fine things said about Grant
by young officers who seemed to know their business.

McClellan laughed. "Not so long as the old-timers haven't
heard of him. Yes, Grant and I are the best the Union has,
but only the youngsters know it, and the rebel generals."

The General asked his guest to observe the new recruits at
drill. It proved a sorry sight: they drilled in foot-deep mud
with wooden guns, and hardly any of the officers knew the
proper words of command. When the 10th and 13th Regi-
ments met on a road, neither commanding officer knew how
to avoid a collision. There was a bloody fist fight before
McClellan spurred his horse into the middle of the melee.

"Soldiers!" he cried. "Spare your blows for the enemies of
your country!"

The words told like bullets, and the fighting stopped
abruptly. Later McClellan told the detective that, despite the
stupidity of Washington officials who expected him to produce fighting men overnight, he meant to create an army
worthy of the name, if it took him a year. "If Washington
leaves me alone to equip and train a real Union army," he
said, "I can win the war within twenty-four months."

"How long do you think the war will last otherwise,
General?"

"Four or five years, definitely," answered McClellan.

McClellan offered the detective a post as major with his
staff for the Department of the Ohio, soon to be formed with
himself in command. The Ohio Department would consist
of the armed forces of three states—Ohio, Illinois and Indiana. Major Pinkerton's duties would be to gather intelligence
information for the department.

It was an important job, and he accepted. The President, after all, had been unable to name a date for the creation of a governmental secret service, and Allan Pinkerton was anxious to play a part in the war effort now. Meanwhile, George Bangs, one of his trusted associates, could take over agency affairs.

McClellan agreed to his request that Timothy Webster be invited to join him in the General's service, along with another half-dozen Pinkerton men. The detective left for Chicago to break the news to his family. It was now late April, 1861, and he was due in Cincinnati to begin his work in mid-May. Meanwhile Timothy Webster, who was anxious to start scouting behind rebel lines, departed for Louisville, with instructions to move southward to Memphis, stopping at Bowling Green and Clarkesville along the way.

The Major's first assignment, after he had reported in Cincinnati, was to determine pro-Union sentiment in the states of Kentucky, Tennessee, Mississippi and Louisiana. McClellan specifically wanted to know if there existed in these states large numbers of southerners who could be counted on to support the Union if Federal armies appeared in their midst. Since railroad schedules were uncertain, "Mr. E. J. Allen of Augusta, Georgia," outfitted himself with a handsome bay capable of outrunning most Confederate horseflesh, and set off south.

He found a certain number of northern sympathizers in Kentucky and Tennessee, though it seemed doubtful to him that Tennessee would remain in the Union. In Nashville he met a number of southern officers, and was able to quash a scheme that might have resulted in hundreds of Union deaths.

One of the officers, an army surgeon, had a plan to fill a number of commissary wagons with whisky that had been liberally mixed with strychnine, a deadly poison. These wagons were then to be abandoned and left on the roads, thus falling into the hands of Federal troops.

The surgeon was a colonel, and despite their chivalrous distaste for the scheme, his junior officers were reluctant to let him know their true opinion of it.

Thinking that Mr. Allen, who seemed to hate the Yankees as much as he did, would praise his lethal stratagem, the colonel asked for his judgment on the matter.

"Colonel," replied the Georgian diplomatically, "it's a deuced fine plan. But there's one thing wrong. You say the poisoned whisky will fall into Union hands. How can you be sure some southern sympathizers—and they are everywhere, thank the Lord—won't take it into their heads to deprive the Yankees of such valuable booty?"

The colonel looked surprised. "I never thought of that, sir. By Jeff Davis, you're right. I don't want any rebel deaths on my conscience. I guess I'll have to forget my little project for one that's just a mite more practical."

The conversation shifted to other matters, and the detective heaved a sigh of relief. Infamous but clever, the colonel's plan might have succeeded all too well.

Leaving Nashville, Mr. Allen rode on to Memphis. There, on the way to his hotel, he came upon a scene that moved him deeply.

Slaves were being sold in the market square. On the auction block men, women and children were being sold to the highest bidder. Wives were callously separated from husbands, children from parents. Nor did he notice any onlookers in the crowd who seemed to disapprove of this brutal traffic in human flesh.

Though he had traveled extensively in the South as an Abolitionist agent, Allan Pinkerton had never come across an actual slave market. The sight turned his stomach. As he moved away, he felt a renewed strength, a more burning belief in the cause for which he fought.

Memphis was being fortified by General Gideon Pillow, and Mr. Allen, after making a number of important friends, had the pleasure of chatting with the General over a brandy and soda at the hotel bar. Pillow was impressed by the forthright Georgian, and spoke freely of his problems. But Mr. Allen found that his best source of information was the Negroes who worked at various military tasks, building earthworks and fortifications, driving the teams and transporting guns and ammunition. Mingling freely with these men, he found them willing and even eager to answer questions.

It was fortunate he had said a few kind words to his Negro stable boy and tipped him generously. On his fifth night in Memphis there was a knock at his door. He opened it to the young colored boy.

"Sir," his visitor said, glancing nervously up and down the corridor, "you better let me in."

Once inside, the lad gave his warning. He had overheard a number of southerners discussing Mr. Allen. One said he had seen him in Cincinnati a few weeks ago, dining with a northern general. "He don't think you a Georgia man, sir," the boy said, "and this very minute he's on his way to get you arrested."

"Thank you, Lem," Mr. Allen said. "Will you do me another favor?"

The boy nodded.

"Do you know the roads leading out of the city?"

"Yes, sir."

"Will you guide me to one of the less-frequented roads leading south?"

"I can do that, yes, sir."

"Good. Saddle my horse immediately, and lead him out to the side of the hotel."

A few minutes later Mr. Allen was on his way to Mississippi, on the theory that his pursuers would be looking for
him on the roads leading east and north. In Jackson, Mississippi, he heard only pro-Secessionist talk and predictions
that Louisiana, too, was bound to leave the Union.

Before departing for Vicksburg, the traveling secret agent
dropped into a Jackson barber shop for a haircut.

The incident taught him a lesson. One of the four barbers,
a German he recognized as a former employee of the Sherman
House in Chicago, hailed him cordially. "Oh, Mr. Pingerdon," the barber said, "vat a pleasure it is to see you! Vat are
you doing here in Jackson?"

The secret agent's blood ran cold. Several customers waiting their turn knew him as E. J. Allen, and one lifted his
head from his newspaper to look at him with a puzzled frown.
Summoning his most imperious look and his southernmost
drawl, Mr. Allen answered the barber: "My man, you are
mistaken. I come from Augusta, Georgia, and I've never been
further north than Richmond in all my life."

The German took a closer look. "Surely, Mr. Pingerdon,
you are mistaken? Don't you remember the Sherman House
in Chicago, and the barber Carl Boehm?"

Mr. Allen got up from his chair angrily and approached
the German's chair. All eyes in the shop were upon him as
he bellowed, "I resent this slur! I demand your apology,
mister, or I'll take that razor out of your hand and cut your
throat with it!"

Though his feelings were plainly hurt, Boehm was quick
to back down. In order to dissolve whatever lingering suspicions still remained, Mr. Allen invited all present, including the barber, to repair to the saloon next door for a series
of toasts to the Confederacy and Jeff Davis. Some time later
he slipped away to the stable where his bay was kept, and
minus a badly needed haircut, set off north toward Cincin-

nati. Things were getting a little too hot for him down south, and Louisiana would have to wait for a more propitious moment.

It was good to see Timothy Webster, who had returned from his own scouting trip south. The star operative had had a chilling series of adventures.

All had gone well until Bowling Green, Kentucky, he told Allan. Posing as a determined rebel who would as soon hang Abe Lincoln as look at him, he had made fast friends in the Kentucky city. These new friends took him for a visit to the rebel camp, where the spy shook hands with recruits, joked and laughed with noncommissioned officers, and discussed strategy with brigadier generals. Meanwhile his eyes were open for any item of intelligence that might be of value to the Union Army.

So popular had the "rebel from Baltimore" become that on his departure from Bowling Green over fifty soldiers and civilians had seen him off at the station, wishing him Godspeed and an early return.

During the train trip to Memphis, Webster noticed that a sharp-faced man, wearing a broad-brimmed hat, was watching him intently. At the east bank of the Tennessee River, where the passengers were obliged to cross by ferry, the sharp-faced man took the conductor aside and talked to him for some time.

Webster had the feeling that he himself had been the object of their conversation. When the train crossed the river, the sharp-faced man disappeared into the dining car, and the detective seized the opportunity to question the conductor.

The man's replies were evasive, except for the admission that the man in the broad-brimmed hat was a member of the Committee of Public Safety, empowered to arrest anyone

suspected of espionage activities on behalf of the North or
even anybody espousing northern sympathies.

Webster nonetheless continued to take notes on the number of troops and heavy guns he saw. At one point the sharp-
featured man approached the vacant seat at his side, but
Webster was prepared. Flipping over the sheet in his mem-
orandum book on which he had been writing, he began
adding a column of figures. The man sat down beside him
but Webster continued his addition. When he got up from
his seat to go to the smoker, he was careful to leave behind a
scribbled reminder to himself reading: "Write Mr. Smith in
Bowling Green about next shipment of bombazine."

When he returned to his seat, both man and reminder had
disappeared. But it appeared that the Committeeman wasn't
to be shaken off that easily. On the platform of the Memphis
station Webster saw him talking to a Confederate officer, who
took a long look in his direction. After Webster had registered at his Memphis hotel, he saw the same officer looking
over the guest book. Evidently the officer had taken over, at
least temporarily, from the man in the broad-brimmed hat.

Expecting to be arrested at any moment for questioning,
Webster memorized as best he could his intelligence notes
taken on the train to Memphis, and then chewed them down.
Returning to the lobby from his room, he was surprised to
see one of his train companions being led away by the officer
in gray. He learned that the man, who had given his home
address as Philadelphia, had been arrested merely because
he was a northerner traveling in the South.

Next morning, at breakfast in the crowded dining room,
Webster joined a table of Confederate officers. The talk
turned to the disaster Federal troops would encounter should
they dare to invade Tennessee. Webster, by now a bosom
friend of the officers, learned the size of Confederate garrisons
at Camp Rector and Fort Harris. Before his new friends left

the table, they invited Webster to visit Camp Rector the next day.

There he was shown the Confederate guns, along with an improved firing device recently developed by Confederate ordnance for certain of its big cannon.

The officers were devastated when Webster announced he was off to Chattanooga to look up a brother he hadn't seen in twelve years. The colonel in command of Camp Rector artillery insisted he return, and offered him a commission in his regiment before some other commanding officer "snapped up so remarkable a gentleman."

The train for Chattanooga left early the next morning. It was Webster's plan to change cars at the junction for a northbound train. No sooner had he done so than he saw his old nemesis, the sharp-featured man in the broad-brimmed hat, staring at him from a nearby seat. Sitting beside the Committeeman was a companion, a huge brute with hands the size of hams.

Webster knew he could be arrested; it was decidedly suspicious for any southerner to be traveling further north than Jackson. When the train arrived in Jackson, Webster stepped out on the platform and spoke to the conductor. For the benefit of his listening enemies, he asked what the best hotel was in the town of Humboldt, on the southern route. He boarded the train for Humboldt, and the two men followed him, taking seats in the same car.

Fifteen minutes before the train arrived in Humboldt, a woman sat down next to Webster and began talking to him in a low, earnest voice. She identified herself as a northern sympathizer and said she had overheard the Committeeman and his henchmen discussing Webster's case. They planned to stay at the same hotel in Humboldt and watch him closely there. If he tried to go northward, they would arrest him and take him to Memphis, where he would be tried as a northern spy.

The woman rose and disappeared before the astonished agent could express his thanks. When the train stopped at Humboldt, Webster got out at the rear end of the car. The man in the broad-brimmed hat and his assistant left by the front.

There was a pile of baggage near him, and Webster quickly hid behind it. His shadows strode rapidly off toward the hotel, under the impression that Webster had a head start.

The express from Memphis left Humboldt a few minutes later, with the spy aboard it on his way north.

When General McClellan came up with another assignment—determining the strength and disposition of Confederate troops in Virginia—Allan Pinkerton chose agent Price Lewis for the job.

Lewis posed as an English lord, and Ian Bridgeman, another Pinkerton operative, as his valet. The snobbish southerners Lewis came in contact with ran themselves ragged in their efforts to properly entertain a bona fide member of the peerage, and Lewis acquired some valuable information—which contributed to the dramatic success of McClellan's brief campaign in Virginia. McClellan, a cautious man, might be inclined to lose many opportunities by needing to be sure he would win a battle before he fought it, but once he had the enemy on the run there was no one who could so decisively turn a retreat into a full-fledged disaster.

The southern armies before Richmond found themselves with a new flank to defend. As a reward McClellan was made Commander-in-Chief of the Union forces, taking over from Winfield Scott. No one was happier at his promotion than Major Allen, who had—it seemed to his wife—found an idol.

She wrote her husband: "I would rather you worshipped

President Lincoln, since I suspect that a general is a hero
only so long as he wins battles, and no general wins them
all." In McClellan's case it was to be a more accurate prophecy
than she knew.

In late July, 1861, George McClellan arrived in Washington to take up his new command. At his side was Major
Allen. The next day both attended a conference called by
Lincoln at which the formation of the first U.S. Secret Service
went through with Major Pinkerton at its head. Placed under
orders from the War Department and General McClellan,
he was given almost unlimited funds, along with a comfort-
able house on I Street to serve as his office and quarters. There
was more than enough room for Joan and Joanie, and the
Major wired his wife to close up the house in Chicago and
join him. The boys were at school in Indiana. Bill was fifteen
now, Bob thirteen.

McClellan, though happy with his new appointment,
found much to criticize in both the current northern plans
for the subjugation of the South and the present condition
of the army in Washington. He believed, as the authorities
in Washington did not, that defeat of the main Confederate
army in Virginia and the capture of Richmond would have
to be accomplished to end the war. And he was disgusted
with the plans General Scott had made for the protection of
the capital city. Disposition of troops there was completely
inadequate, and nothing prevented the enemy from shelling
the city from nearby heights. Why were the streets of Washington filled with straggling officers and men, some of them
absent without leave? The lack of discipline and organization
was horrifying.

"I mean to make a modern army out of all this chaos, and
I will!" the General said, slamming his fist down on the table.

"In order to do that," said Pinkerton, "you'll have to get
rid of the political appointees who hold important military

offices. Can you survive all the enemies that will make for you?"

The General grinned, obviously struck by the practical good sense of Pinkerton's comment. "Better watch out, Major," he told him. "If you keep on being so good a strategist, I'll make you my chief of staff."

The day after Joan arrived, a visitor was shown into the Major's office.

"Hello, Dad," Bill Pinkerton said airily, "you've gained a little weight."

"Bill, what on earth are you doing in Washington? You're supposed to be at school!"

"There's a war on, Dad," Bill said, as if reminding him of a rather obvious fact, and looked around the room. "No pictures up yet, I see. How's Mother?"

The Major looked at this sturdily built, fifteen-year-old son who was a carbon copy of himself. He knew why Bill had come to Washington: to join the Secret Service. Should he send him back to school? Would he go?

"I want to work with you, Dad," Bill said. "I hope you won't argue about it, because I'm here to stay."

"Is that so?"

Bill nodded, lifting a jaw that was as obstinate, the Major thought, as his own.

Bill said, "Think what great experience the Secret Service would be for my work later on at the agency."

"That's true," his father admitted. "But there's one difficulty. You're not yet sixteen. I'll have to get special permission from the President and, of course, from your mother." Maybe one or both would refuse.

"Oh, Mother's no problem." Bill got to his feet. "Let's go see the President now."

"Hold on there, lad. Lincoln isn't as easy to see as all that. I'll have to write him a letter."

Bill reached for a pencil and paper. "Go ahead, Dad, I'm ready for your dictation. How do you address him? 'Dear Mr. President' or 'Dear Abe'?"

Pinkerton didn't write President Lincoln that day, but shortly afterward a note went to the President from I Street regarding William. Joan Pinkerton had already agreed to let Bill join the Secret Service provided he took no part in espionage activities that could conceivably end with a rebel rope around his neck. Nevertheless, and without his father's permission, Bill went on scouting parties and once narrowly avoided capture while in civilian dress. Hearing of this, his mother insisted her adventurous son be given a desk job at the I Street house. Here Bill acquitted himself reluctantly, but well.

Though the Chief of Secret Service worked a sixteen-hour day, he believed in relaxation. Every afternoon he took an hour-long carriage ride, regardless of the weather. He was in charge of military espionage, counterespionage and a department called "general intelligence"; before the cases of deserters, refugees and prisoners of war were decided, he personally interviewed every one. But his chief and most immediate responsibility was rebel spies in Washington. The capital was swarming with them, and it would be some time before the new department would be able to cope with the well-entrenched southern agents.

Ready or not, he received orders to obtain evidence on a known Confederate spy which would justify search of her house in Washington. The spy was Rose Greenhow, a beautiful and wealthy widow who made no secret of her Secessionist sympathies. Mrs. Greenhow had not only secured copies of Assistant Secretary of War Thomas A. Scott's minutes written during a meeting with ranking Union generals, but less than twenty-four hours later had delivered them to the rebels in Richmond. The northern battle plans she sent to General Beauregard before the Battle of Bull Run had done much to make the Confederate victory possible. To Rose Greenhow opening guarded War Department files was child's play.

Yet despite the government's knowledge of her treasonable activities, Mrs. Greenhow's social prestige in Washington was so high that any attempt to trap her had to be made with the greatest possible caution. Her sister was married to a nephew of Dolley Madison, wife of the fourth President, and her brother-in-law was the second Comptroller of the U. S. Treasury. She was Washington's leading hostess of the Democratic party.

Every night for a week Major Allen and two of his men kept close watch on the Greenhow house at Thirteenth and I. The vigil proved both tedious and unrewarding. Since Mrs. Greenhow's parlor windows were too high up for the Chief to see into them from the ground, the Major took to standing, with boots removed, on his men's shoulders.

From this vantage point he could see Rose Greenhow and her elegant parlor. One rainy night a young captain in Federal uniform joined the widow on her sofa. It was obvious he was infatuated with her, so much so that after the widow had allowed herself to be kissed on the cheek, the officer took a map from his pocket—evidently a military map—and proceeded to point things out to his attentive companion.

Barely able to contain his anger, Major Allen watched the scene. Even the pelting rain failed to dampen his rage. Men in blue had died by the thousands at Bull Run, and here this garrison soldier sat giving military secrets to the enemy.

Mrs. Greenhow folded the map and put it away in a pocket of her gown. A moment later the officer rose to leave.

"He's going—let me down!" ordered the Major. His operatives were only too glad to deposit their burden to the ground.

As Major Allen set off in pursuit of the traitor, one of his men yelled after him, "Chief, you forgot your boots!" But it was too late—the Major had already disappeared into the darkness and the rain.

It was only after he lost his quarry in the downpour that the Major realized he had left his boots behind. He was plodding back to Mrs. Greenhow's when a passing military patrol decided to check the credentials of this bootless character.

"I have no identification with me," he told the lieutenant in command, "but if you'll get in touch with Secretary Scott of the War Department, he'll vouch for me."

The lieutenant laughed. "Sergeant Maloney, bring this madman to Captain Ellis. He'll know what to do with him."

The Secret Service Chief was marched twelve blocks through the downpour to the nearest command post. There, to his mingled amazement and gratification, he was confronted by none other than the young officer he had seen in Rose Greenhow's parlor.

Captain Ellis evidently had a reputation for forcing confessions at the point of a gun. Major Allen found himself looking down the barrel of a derringer. He was told that rebel spies deserved worse than a bullet in the neck.

The prisoner smiled. "Captain," he said, "I couldn't agree with you more."

The Captain holstered his revolver with a grunt of disgust. "Sergeant, take this man to the detention cells at the Capital City Jail. The provost will deal with him in the morning."

At the city jail the Chief asked a good-natured guard for pen and paper. In the flickering light of a candle he wrote messages to his wife and to Assistant War Secretary Scott. The latter read: "Please arrange my release quietly so there is absolutely no discussion. I will explain later. E. J. Allen."

The guard agreed to deliver the notes when he went off

duty, and the Chief lay back on his straw pallet in his damp clothes, to get whatever sleep he could.

He was freed the next morning. At the War Department he persuaded Secretary Scott to postpone Mrs. Greenhow's and Captain Ellis' arrests until he could learn how the woman spy arranged to put the information into Confederate hands. But after a week the impatient Scott ordered her house to be searched from basement to attic. On the basis of the incriminating material found there, she and Captain Ellis were arrested.

The Captain was jailed at Fort McHenry, but Mrs. Greenhow had better luck. Thanks to the intercession of powerful friends, she was passed through the lines to Richmond. From there she continued to serve the Confederate cause.

Though Major Allen was commended for his work in the Greenhow case, he was very dissatisfied with the way it had gone. He was fond of saying, "About all the Federal government realized from the Greenhow case was a lovesick traitor, and about all Allan Pinkerton caught was a bad cold."

7 Timothy Webster's Close Shaves

IN SEPTEMBER, 1861, TIMOTHY WEBSTER SET OFF AGAIN FOR Baltimore. There he picked up a number of letters and messages entrusted to him by southerners for delivery north to relatives and friends. Needless to say, Major Allen read—and very profitably—all of these letters and messages before sending them on. When Webster reappeared in Baltimore his reputation as a courier for whom northern pickets and provost marshals were child's play was firmly established, and his status was close to that of a hero.

He was asked to join the Knights of Liberty, a Secessionist secret society whose membership was carefully restricted, and of course he was delighted.

The society observed elaborate security precautions. Webster was taken blindfolded to a remote section of the city, then led to a building whose door swung open only after the exchange of several passwords. Still blindfolded, he was brought to a large room where he satisfied questioners as to the purity of his desire to become a member of the knightly band. He then took an oath of loyalty. Swords clanked as they were returned to their scabbards, and the new Knight was bidden to rise.

His blindfold removed, Webster noticed that the forty-odd men in the room were of the better class of Secessionist; few of them had, so far, been suspected of disloyalty to the Union. Webster was asked to talk on his recent mission, and sat down to loud applause. Then the meeting resumed its regular business. Webster was dumfounded to learn that a plot was now in preparation for an uprising against Washington. The Knights claimed that close to ten thousand Baltimoreans were ready to take up arms at a moment's notice and join the rebel army when it arrived in Maryland. Moreover, it appeared that the Baltimoreans did not stand alone in their plot against the government. Branches of the Knights of Liberty existed in a number of outlying towns, and Secessionists of the entire state were working closely with them. There was no lack of arms.

After the meeting Webster left immediately for Washington to consult with his Chief.

Like Webster, Allan Pinkerton was reluctant to shrug off the plot as merely a visionary scheme which had little chance of success. "These Knights are dangerous, and we must try to destroy them, whether or not the rebels advance into Maryland. I'll alert General McClellan and the Secretary of War. Meanwhile, go to the meetings, learn all you can, and report to me as often as possible. One more thing. Do you think you can help some of our other men infiltrate the society?"

Webster looked doubtful. "I don't think so, Chief. The Knights are careful about their bedfellows. A lot more so than the Palmettos."

"Suppose we work it this way: you point out the leaders to some of our operatives, and they'll try to talk their way into an invitation to join."

"Nothing ventured, nothing gained," agreed Webster.

The Major's strategy worked. Overconfident, the Knights relaxed their vigilance, and two more Pinkerton men managed to join the secret society within a few weeks of voicing proslavery sympathies in the better Baltimore saloons. Webster and his two colleagues attended the midnight meetings regularly, gaining valuable information on southern military plans.

By society rules no one could enter the conspirators' inside chamber without passing two guards and giving the current passwords. The guards were appointed by the chief Knight from among volunteers. It was the Pinkerton plan to wait for a night when two of his men were on guard duty.

Exactly at midnight on November 28, a noise like that of a battering ram interrupted a speech being made by Mr. Timothy Webster to the assembled Knights. The door burst open with a crash, and a stream of bluecoated soldiers, all heavily armed, took up positions around the room, cutting off any possibility of escape.

When the men were marched in a body before the provost marshal, it was noticed that only one of them, Timothy Webster, had managed to slip away. Leaders of the conspiracy were taken to Fort McHenry, along with those who refused to take an oath of allegiance to the Union. The rest, after questioning, were released on parole.

With the arrest of the Baltimore Knights of Liberty, the entire statewide organization collapsed. Even if in the next months Confederate troops had marched on Washington, there would have been few Knights of Liberty to join them. Their swords were broken and their plumes dragged in the dust.

Webster disappeared from Baltimore long enough to indicate he had a healthy respect for Yankee justice. He then turned up at the fashionable Miller's Hotel with a span of fine horses and an elegant carriage. Before long he was the center and leading figure of a new group of serious, if not fanatical, Secessionists. His handsome horses became well-known at the races, and he was a special favorite with the ladies.

During this time he concentrated on uncovering the secret plots and maneuvers of persons disloyal to the Union. He unmasked several people whose loyalty had never been questioned. That some were members of his group bothered the softhearted spy, and at one point he incurred the wrath of Allan Pinkerton by protecting a lady whose information on Union installations in Baltimore had proved valuable to Johnny Reb.

"Timothy," the Chief stormed at him, "you're the best man I have, but you've got to remember these people aren't really your friends!"

Once Webster returned to Baltimore after a longer absence than usual. He was entertaining friends at a fashionable saloon when a men named Bill Zigler walked in. Zigler, one of the ringleaders of the mob that had attacked Union troops last April, was a bully and a tough.

He stopped in the middle of the room and barked, "Webster, I've been looking for you!"

"I wish you hadn't found me," Webster answered, and the men laughed.

"If I hadn't," Zigler replied darkly, "the Committee of Public Safety would have found you for me. Webster, you can't get away with it anymore."

The spy pretended puzzlement, and Zigler turned toward the watching men.

"Gentlemen," he said loudly, "this man is a spy."

There was a deathlike silence. Then one of Webster's friends spoke up. "Zigler, you must be drunk. There's no better southern man in Baltimore than Webster here."

Zigler grinned contemptuously. "If that's true, then ask him what he was doing in Washington yesterday, talking with the Chief of the Secret Service."

For a moment Webster felt himself lost; he was completely

unprepared for Zigler's attack. But he realized he had to shout louder than his antagonist.

He went up to the man, and taking him by the lapels, yelled as if in an uncontrollable rage: "Zigler, you are a liar and a scoundrel!"

The tough knocked down Webster's hands and, with a gasp of rage, went for his throat.

Webster was not going to be unprepared a second time. His fist lashed out and struck Zigler between the eyes. The southerner fell to the floor with a thud.

But he was far from finished. Reaching for a wicked-looking knife, he picked himself up and rushed for Webster.

"Stop!" cried the spy. A revolver had suddenly appeared in his hand. "Another step, and I'll blow your stupid brains out!"

Zigler hesitated, and Webster took full advantage. "You coward!" he shouted, "I'd be right to shoot you down like a dog. And I will unless you leave this place immediately."

Zigler put his knife away and headed for the door. There he turned, long enough to glare back at Webster and say, "I'll fix you yet, traitor! Just watch out!"

One of his companions slapped Webster on the shoulder as Zigler left the saloon. "Forget it, friend. Why I'd as soon suspect Jeff Davis of being a Yankee spy as good old Tim Webster!"

Another nodded agreement. "Tim, nothing that gutter rat said can hurt you with us. Let's forget what happened, and have another drink."

The affair ended in jokes and laughter. Far from compromising Webster, the incident rather raised him higher in the estimation of his friends.

A short time later Webster, well-known in Baltimore as a man who could be counted upon to get letters and other communications through Union lines, was approached by a man named McPhail for a similar errand. McPhail wanted to send a draft for a large amount of money to Richmond and offered Webster a generous commission to do the job.

Webster suspected McPhail of being a Union agent, but since a mutual southern friend was present at their discussion, there was no way to identify himself as a member of the same camp.

Webster agreed to carry the bank draft to Richmond in two days time. The next morning he was taking an early morning constitutional when he felt a hand on his arm. He turned, to see McPhail's threatening face. "Webster," he said, "you're my prisoner. Since we're directly in front of the station house, there's no sense your making any fuss about it."

"You fool," Webster told him, "I'm a member of the Secret Service!"

"See if you can convince the captain of that," McPhail said drily, and ordered the two soldiers standing guard at the door to take Webster inside.

Webster's attempt to explain his predicament to the captain was unsuccessful. "I have no time now to talk to rebels," he said shortly, and told a sergeant to put Webster in a cell.

The detective clamored to be heard, but there was no response from the captain. Finally he determined to get himself released by any means he could. Calling over the messenger boy, who ran errands for the soldiers, he handed him a five-dollar bill. "The money's yours if you'll send that wire I've written."

"What telegram?" the boy asked. "I don't see none."

"Its rolled up inside the bill."

The lad nodded and disappeared for the rest of the day. Webster had no idea if he had sent the wire. Five hours later, a lieutenant from the provost marshal's appeared at the door of Webster's cell. He was trying to hide a grin.

"Timothy Webster?" he asked.

"That's right, Lieutenant."

"You're to be taken to Fort McHenry."

Something in the tone of the lieutenant's voice, not to mention his grin, told Webster that Allan Pinkerton had come to his rescue, and that everything was all right.

Under guard he was taken to the street, where a covered van was waiting. Webster and his two guards got in, and the officer said loudly, "Direct to Fort McHenry!"

When they were under way, the officer apologized to Webster for his arrest, and said that it had been arranged for him to escape. When he gave the word, Webster was to jump from the wagon and make his way to his rebel friends. After remaining with them for a few days he was to report to Major Allen in Washington.

"Has McPhail been told to let me alone in future?" Webster asked him.

The lieutenant nodded.

"Well, that's a consolation."

At the lieutenant's nod Webster jumped from the wagon, which had conveniently slowed down. Two soldiers fired their rifles into the air as the spy headed down an alley. An hour later he was knocking at the door of a Secessionist friend, Sam Sloan.

Sloan was amazed at his escape. He insisted upon calling in some of their mutual friends for a celebration, and Webster was toasted into the early hours for his cleverness and courage.

Next day the newspapers carried reports of the escape, one of them concluding: "It is not known what direction Webster took, but we are confident he will be unable to escape from the city."

Webster reported to his chief in Washington, who had a new assignment for him. Two days later he left on a trip to Virginia with John Scobell, a newly recruited Negro agent.

The two separated at Leonardstown. Scobell made his way to the rebel camp at Dumfries, and Webster stayed on in Leonardstown for a few days, hoping something would turn up to his advantage.

It did the next day, when Webster was introduced to Dr. Gurley, a fellow guest at the hotel who had been described to him as a deserter from the Yankees. A southerner, and lately a surgeon who had served in the regular Union Army, Gurley wanted to throw up his commission and join the rebel side in Richmond.

Gurley confided to Webster that he was carrying important dispatches from northern Copperheads to Judah Benjamin, Confederate Secretary of War. His problem lay in getting safely past the Union pickets outside Richmond.

"Doctor," Webster told him, "I will guarantee you passage through the northern lines."

The detective had arranged to meet Scobell every few days, and at their next meeting he revealed his plan to relieve Dr. Gurley of his dispatches. Scobell was more than willing.

Webster told Gurley he had found a small-boat captain who would ferry him across the Potomac. At twilight of the following day, he and the Doctor left on the two-mile trip upriver to the captain's landing. They reached it, only to discover that the captain wasn't expected for another hour. The impatient Doctor took a walk in a nearby patch of woodland to calm his nerves.

Scobell was waiting there, and with his pistol butt knocked the unfortunate Doctor on the head. Within minutes the secret dispatches, meant for Judah Benjamin, were on their way to Allan Pinkerton in Washington, carried by Scobell.

Webster consoled the soreheaded Doctor, who in no way connected him with the incident. He promised Dr. Gurley they could cross the river the following night. The detective was as good as his word, and he and Gurley joined friends in Richmond a day later. The trip wasn't an entirely wasted one for Timothy Webster. He collected information on the disposition of rebel forces around Fredericksburg and received a pass from Judah Benjamin which permitted him to travel at will anywhere behind Confederate lines.

Major Allen used relatively few female agents during the Civil War, but those he did use performed important services.

Mrs. Emily Baker was sent south in November, 1861, by the Secret Service, to investigate the Tredegar Ironworks in Richmond, largest munitions and weapons plant in the South. The detective had reason to believe the ironworks was turning out a new type of torpedo, about which it was essential that the North have information.

Mrs. Baker had at one time lived in Richmond, and it was a simple matter for her to get a pass permitting her to go there for the purpose of visiting old friends. While in the Confederate capital she was the guest of a Captain Atwater and his wife. The Captain, in the rebel artillery, was a zealous partisan of the Secessionist cause. Mrs. Baker allowed him to think he was winning her over to it.

The Tredegar Ironworks was off limits to civilians, but Atwater finally arranged a visit for Mrs. Baker on the understanding that she was forbidden to take notes or make sketches. On the day she was scheduled to visit the ironworks, Atwater returned home with his apologies. He would be unable to take her to the works today, since his presence was required downriver at some submarine battery tests.

What were submarine batteries, the wide-eyed Mrs. Baker wanted to know. Atwater explained they were an experimental device calculated to destroy the Union fleet now blockading the mouth of the James River.

The visitor from Washington wondered if she could observe the experiment, that is, if there was no danger involved.

Atwater was certain there was not. He would be delighted to bring his guest along to the experimental site.

There Mrs. Baker learned that the device being tested was a working model of one considerably larger being completed at the Tredegar plant. It was a small submarine which, approaching an old scow moored in the middle of the river, attached to it a gunpowder-filled magazine. The magazine was fired by a specially constructed fuse, set off by the submarine from a safe distance. The only indication of the submerged submarine was a small green-painted float, which remained above the water and supplied the three-man submarine crew with air.

The experiment was a decided success. The scow blew up with an ear-splitting crash, and a few minutes later the submarine emerged to rousing cheers.

Returning to the Atwaters that afternoon, Mrs. Baker drew a sketch of the green float and sewed it into her bonnet. A few days later she was taken on a tour of the Tredegar Ironworks. Though not permitted to view the full-size submarine, she did catch a glimpse of the accompanying green air float.

Two days later she was in Washington, delivering the sketch to Allan Pinkerton, who turned it over to General McClellan. The General passed it on to the Navy Department. Word was sent to the northern fleet at the mouth of the James to keep an extrasharp lookout for green floats that seemed to be connected to nothing in particular. As a result, drag ropes from a vessel of the blockading fleet caught the air tubes of one innocent-appearing float, no doubt drowning all on board the submarine. The Union blockade continued, unthreatened and intact.

8 A Great Spy Dies, and the Reno Gang

SHORTLY BEFORE MCCLELLAN LAUNCHED HIS PENINSULAR Campaign for the capture of Richmond, Timothy Webster disappeared in the direction of the rebel capital. Weeks passed, and there was no word from him. Major Allen called for volunteers to make inquiries about his missing operative and come to his rescue, if necessary.

Six Pinkerton men, all friends or admirers of Webster, presented themselves. Two were chosen—John Scully and Price Lewis. On the face of it, their qualifications were good. Both had worked with Webster on missions in the South, and were known by Secessionists to be his friends. Scully was of Irish birth, Lewis of English parentage. They could thus convincingly present themselves in Richmond as neutrals.

Yet in choosing them Allan Pinkerton made a fatal mistake. Scully and Lewis had been used not only as spies, but as counterspies. They had helped search the Washington homes of many southern sympathizers who had since left the northern capital for Richmond, and could easily be recognized by them as Union detectives.

The two men arrived in Richmond and took rooms at the Exchange Hotel. That afternoon they visited the offices of

The Richmond Enquirer, to which Webster had contributed some purple prose in praise of southern virtues.

When Scully and Lewis asked for Webster, the editor casually told them where he could be found—at a hotel only a few blocks away. He lay ill there, with a severe case of rheumatism.

They found Webster in a badly weakened state. One of his southern friends, a Mr. Pierce, was at his bedside. While Pierce chatted with Lewis, Webster told Scully, in no uncertain terms, that he considered his and Lewis' presence in Richmond highly dangerous to all concerned. If they were to come under suspicion, so would he. He advised the pair to leave the city immediately.

"It's the Chief's orders," Scully explained. "We have instructions to get you out of Richmond—at any cost."

Pierce seemed in no hurry to leave, and the agents departed, saying they would return that afternoon.

Their second visit justified all Webster's fears and resulted in disaster. This time Webster's visitors were two other Confederate friends, a Captain McCallum of the Richmond garrison and Chase Morton of Washington. Though the detectives did not remember Morton, the young southerner recognized them as the agents who had searched his parents' house in the capital city. When the northerners left the hotel an hour later, a provost marshal's detail was waiting for them on the sidewalk.

Confederate justice was swift and ruthless. Within a week Scully and Lewis, identified by the whole Morton family, had been tried and sentenced to death. Led astray by clever rebel interrogators, the pair were convinced they could do nothing to save Webster, but might be able to save themselves with full confessions. They did so, implicating Webster, who, up to that time, was free and clear. The sick man was taken into custody.

On April 18, 1862, Timothy Webster was convicted of espionage and sentenced to be hung. Richmond newspapers headlined the story.

Allan Pinkerton, who had been following events in Richmond with a mounting sense of horror, rushed to Washington to confer with President Lincoln and the new Secretary of War, Edwin Stanton. Stanton framed a letter intimating that if the rebels executed the three northern agents, the Federal government would show no mercy to southern agents now in northern hands.

The Secret Service Chief was dissatisfied with Stanton's letter. "Mr. Secretary," he told him, "we cannot afford to imply, we must threaten. This is no time for diplomacy."

The terrible-tongued Stanton was offended. "I do not tell you how to write your letters, sir," he said icily. "Do not tell me how to write mine." Though a brilliant, able man, Stanton had a formidable weakness—he took criticism badly.

Had McClellan moved faster toward Richmond, he might have been able to capture both the city and Timothy Webster. But "Little Mac" was forced to fall back, and retreated in a masterly fashion to Harrison's Landing. Though the sentences of Lewis and Scully were commuted, Webster went to his death on the scaffold with a smile on his wan and ravaged face.

Crushed by the blow, Allan Pinkerton threw himself desperately into work, hoping to avenge Webster's death by amassing more and more intelligence of the enemy who had killed his best man and taken from him a valued friend. Later he had his body removed from a Richmond cemetery and reburied near the Pinkerton family plot in Chicago. The stone he erected bore this epitaph:

SACRED
to the Memory of
TIMOTHY WEBSTER
Who
Was Executed as a Spy
by the
REBELS, IN RICHMOND, VA.,
April 29, 1862
AFTER GALLANT SERVICE IN THE WAR
OF THE REBELLION.
HE SEALED HIS FIDELITY AND DEVOTION
TO HIS COUNTRY
WITH HIS BLOOD.
Alike to him are the heats of summer, or the
snows of winter. Peacefully and quietly he
sleeps. The Spy of the Rebellion is at rest.

Hearing that Major Allen was working an eighteen-hour day at the house on I Street, General McClellan called him out into the field, where he could keep an eye on him. It was no use. Major Allen slipped away to join scouting parties, and on one of them had his horse shot from under him.

"Allan, I insist you keep to camp," McClellan told him. "Your life is too valuable to be whisked away by a sniper's bullet."

The Battle of Antietam, the bitterest and costliest yet, was fought on September 17. Lee saved his army, but it was completely crippled, and the rebel invasion of the North was over. Lincoln, however, believed McClellan should have pursued Lee and destroyed him, and when "Little Mac" had the arrogance to demand additional reinforcements, removed him from the top command. General Ambrose E. Burnside was put in his place.

Pinkerton went to see the deposed General at headquarters. He could not hide his pain nor his anger at Lincoln for choosing to persecute the only military man who in his opinion was certain to win the war.

"Doesn't the President realize that the only reason you didn't follow Lee was because you feared he would have marched on Washington had he beaten you? Lincoln's let the politicians destroy the best man he has."

McClellan waved his hand wearily. "Water under the bridge, Allan. You'll do me a favor by letting your criticisms of the President stop here. They won't help General Burnside."

"I intend to resign," Allen said.

"Lincoln will be generous enough to ignore your resignation. Good luck, Allan."

As McClellan had predicted, the President chose to ignore the resignation of his Chief of Secret Service, feeling that his resentment would eventually cool—which it did.

Although Allan Pinkerton turned his military espionage department over to the capable Colonel Lafayette Baker, and moved his wife and daughter back to Chicago, he continued in Federal service until peace was declared, investigating damage claims in various parts of the country. At least two Pinkertons served in the Secret Service until the war's end; in 1865 Bill was joined by Bob, whose work behind enemy lines earned Colonel Baker's commendation.

No longer connected with the Secret Service, the ex-chief nevertheless was successful in uncovering a plot to free 7500 rebel prisoners interned at Camp Douglas, near Chicago. And the day after Abraham Lincoln's assassination, he telegraphed Secretary Stanton his sense of loss and his crushing regret that he had not been at Ford's Theater to protect the President.

New Orleans, La.
April 19, 1865

Hon. Edward M. Stanton, Secretary of War:

This morning's papers contained the awful intelligence of the assassination of President Lincoln. . . . Under the providence of God, in February, 1861, I was enabled to save him from the fate he now has met. How I regret that I had not been near him previous to this fatal act. I might have had the means to arrest it. If I can be of any service, please let me know. The service of my whole force, or life itself, is at your disposal and I trust you will excuse me for impressing upon you the necessity of great personal caution on your part. At this time the nation cannot spare you.

E. J. Allen

During the war the Chicago office had kept the traveling claims investigator fully informed of agency affairs. Business had fallen off sharply after 1861, chiefly due to the fact that most of the agency's best operatives were working with the Secret Service; but in March, 1863, when train robbers stole $100,000 in Adams Express Company money as well as bank drafts from a Northern Central train, a major case was thrown into its lap. Allan Pinkerton took a leave of absence from his government duties, and directed the investigation. Efficiently, without fireworks or melodrama, a small but well-drilled team of Pinkerton men swung into action. Within a month the criminals were rounded up, and close to $90,000 was returned to Adams Express.

One newspaper account referred admiringly to the agency as "The Private Eye that sees all and never blinks." The anonymous writer had no idea at the time that he was coining a phrase descriptive of the private detective that would pass into the language when, later, people were to call detectives "private eyes."

As usual, after the solution of a well-publicized crime, the Chicago office was deluged with job applications. Some were thrown into what the Chief called his "Lunatic File." One man said he was sure he would make a "fine detective" because he had "nothing better to do" with his time. Another knew he was meant to be a Pinkerton operative because he could always tell when his wife was lying to him. Still another offered himself and his "good bird dog." Describing this kind of job applicant, Pinkerton later wrote: "There seem to be three things that are the ambition of a great class of people who are either in need of employment or who are dissatisfied with the employment they have. They wish to go on the stage, or become an author, or turn detective. It is about an equal chance which way they will go."

Nothing contributed more to the success of the agency's work in the Adams Express case than the Pinkerton's National criminal file, started by the Chief before the war. The file, foreunner of the modern rogues' gallery, bulged with facts on thousands of known criminals. It included photographs and full biographies, and noted not only a subject's physical characteristics, but his special methods of operation and his likely companions and hideouts. Until the Bertillon system of identification through body measurements and hair and skin coloring was adopted by American law enforcement agencies in 1886, police from all over the nation were constantly in touch with the agency for this unique and essential information.

On April 10, 1865, Allan Pinkerton received the thanks of Adams Express in the form of a framed receipt for the stolen money. It was an auspicious date, symbolizing resumption of the detective's regular careeer. The day before, at a courthouse in Appomattox County, Virginia, General Ulysses S. Grant had accepted General Lee's surrender.

Renegades and outlaws on both sides of the Mason-Dixon Line had used the Civil War as an excuse for the robberies and murders committed in the name of patriotism. When the Confederacy surrendered, some of these bandits on the rebel side resolved to "fight on"; others, both ex-Gray and ex-Blue, knew they wouldn't be allowed to give themselves up.

The five Reno brothers of Seymour, Indiana, had fought for the Blue, but not for long. By 1863 all of them had deserted and returned home to Jackson County. There, by threatening criminals with death unless they joined the Reno standard, they organized the country's first great outlaw band. Almost a hundred safecrackers, murderers, gunmen, train-robbers and counterfeiters agreed to take orders from John Reno and his brothers, Frank, William, Simeon and Clint. There was also a female Reno, Laura, a handsome young woman who could ride as fast and shoot as straight as any of her brothers.

By the spring of 1866 the Reno boys were the uncrowned kings of Jackson County, and the unmolested terror of three states—Indiana, Illinois and Missouri. No witnesses could be found to testify against them, and the brothers, no mean politicians themselves, had arranged the election of officials so corrupt or weak that the Renos and their criminal associates escaped prosecution.

In late 1866, the office of the county treasurer at Gallatin, Missouri, was robbed of $23,000 by a group of men identified by witnesses as the Renos. Allan Pinkerton was asked to take the case.

George Bangs, general manager of the agency's Chicago branch, tried to talk him out of it. "Seymour is an armed camp," he reminded the Chief. "Do you realize how difficult it's going to be to fight the Renos in their own territory? And we're risking the lives of our men."

The Chief nodded. "I know it's a tough job, George, but no organization worth its name ever avoided a challenge."

The Chief's strategy with the Renos was to remove the brothers from Jackson County, where the law was powerless to deal with them. After obtaining a writ of requisition from the state of Indiana, he laid careful plans. Three operatives, two of them bluff, brawny men likely to hit it off with the Renos, drifted into Seymour at roughly the same time. One of them, Robert Winscott, opened a saloon. Another, Phil Oates, cheerfully identified himself as a gambler and settled in at the local hotel. A third, Walter Meara, found work as a freight handler at the railroad station.

This wasn't the first time the Chief had used operatives— some unfriendly critics called them spies—to work from within in hopes of gaining a suspect's friendship and confidence. "Severe moralists," he later wrote, "have found this method distasteful, and question whether it is either legitimate or defensible. Certainly it is distasteful. But the office of the detective is to serve the ends of justice, to purge society of the degrading influences of crime, and to protect the lives, property and honor of the community at large. In this righteous work the end will unquestionably justify the means adopted to secure the desired result."

Results, in the Reno case, were not long in coming. One evening John Reno dropped in at Winscott's saloon. Phil Oates was there, and the three men got to talking. Winscott brought the conversation around to trains, on which John Reno considered himself an authority.

"Number thirty-one's due in tonight at the depot, isn't it, John?" Oates asked the outlaw.

Reno shook his head. "No, it's Number twenty-nine, from Indianapolis. Number thirty-one came through this afternoon."

Oates turned to Winscott. "Bob, what do you say? Is it my train that's due, or John's?"

"Don't know, Phil," the saloonkeeper answered.

Oates laid a twenty-dollar bill on the bar. He said to Reno: "John, I'll bet you this twenty dollars it's Number thirty-one that's going to pull in"—he took out his watch—"in exactly ten minutes."

Reno placed a twenty-dollar bill over Oates'. "You've got yourself a bet. Bob, will you hold the money while we're down at the depot watching that train come in?"

Winscott untied his apron. "I'll do better than that, John. I'll go down to the station with you."

At the depot Walter Meara, the freight handler, emerged from the shadows to join the three men. They swapped train yarns until the lights of the next arrival showed around the bend. Then, to John Reno's great surprise, he saw that Winscott and Oates held revolvers aimed at his stomach.

"What's this mean, fellows?" Reno asked uneasily. "You playin' a joke?"

"You're under arrest, John," Wescott told him.

The outlaw turned to Meara. "Walter," he pleaded, "can't you do something? These men are crazy."

Meara stared impassively at him.

The train pulled in—it was Number twenty-nine—and four deputies from Daviess County, Missouri, jumped off, followed by a squarely built, bearded man in his middle forties.

Allan Pinkerton showed his requisition papers to John Reno and told him he was being returned to Missouri to answer charges of burglary. It was then the badman decided to act. He struck out with his powerful fists and bellowed for help at the top of his lungs. A few men came running from a nearby lunchroom, but by that time John Reno had been carried, kicking, aboard the train.

Openmouthed, the onlookers watched Number twenty-nine leave Seymour. Then, one ran to the Renos' hotel to give the alarm.

The Reno brothers commandeered an idle locomotive and gave pursuit, but they were much too late. John Reno was tried and convicted of robbery at Gallatin and sentenced to twenty-five years in the state penitentiary.

Though the arrest made headlines, the detective chief knew his work to destroy the Reno gang had only begun. Frank, who had taken over the leadership of the gang, was as dangerous as John, and a more determined fighter, and the brothers still held the town of Seymour in their vicious grip.

The Renos lay low for a few months, and then struck again in a series of raids in Indiana and Missouri, robbing stores, county treasury offices and post offices. Nor did they slight the railroads. So many trains were held up in Indiana that the people of Seymour were saying, after opening their morning papers, "Well, it's safe to travel again for a while. The Renos got another train last night, and everybody knows they don't hit more than one a week."

Early in 1868, Frank Reno led a band of seven men across the state line and robbed the bank at Magnolia, Iowa, of $15,000. County officials wired Allan Pinkerton, begging him to take the case. The detective arrived in Magnolia a few days later with Bill Pinkerton (he and Bob had joined the agency in 1865) and two assistants.

After several days of questioning railroad men and townspeople, the detectives discovered that the gang had fled Magnolia on a stolen handcar. Bill Pinkerton and an aide hired a buggy and traced the thieves to Council Bluffs—thirty-five miles from the scene of the robbery. There was no sign of the bandits in Council Bluffs, but it was likely they still were there. At least, Allan Pinkerton knew they had not yet returned to Seymour.

"The Renos must be staying with an accomplice in Council Bluffs," he told Bill. "Make some inquiries about a possible former resident of Seymour."

The hunch paid off. Bill brought news of a saloon in Council Bluffs owned by a disreputable character named Brown who had once lived in Seymour. A day-and-night watch on the premises turned up an unusual catch—a wealthy citizen and pillar of the church named Michael Rogers. Rogers' background was swiftly investigated, and it developed that not only did the churchman have a criminal record which he had hitherto successfully hidden, but he had paid his taxes at the county treasurer's office the day before the robbery.

"That," deduced Bill, "gave him a fine chance to make sure the money was there and to memorize the office entrances and exits."

His father agreed. "Rogers should lead us to the Renos. Put a watch on his house."

The next day, just after dawn, Bill Pinkerton saw four men, led by Frank Reno and Rogers, hurry into Rogers' house by the back door. Reno was carrying a satchel. A few hours later Allan Pinkerton, at his hotel headquarters in Council Bluffs, learned that the Mills County treasury at Glenwood, thirty miles away, had been burglarized by five men. Almost $13,000 had been stolen.

The detective chief had difficulty getting a warrant to search Rogers' house. At first the local authorities laughed at the suggestion that the town's leading citizen was a common criminal. But the skeptical Pottawattamie County sheriff finally gave in.

Next morning the Pinkertons, along with their two assistants and the sheriff, called on Michael Rogers. He was having breakfast. Frank Reno and two of his gang were enjoying after-breakfast cigars.

Rogers, an impressive man, rose to his full height of six foot one.

"Sir," he told the detective, "you have invaded my privacy and that of my family. I intend to sue you for every cent you've got."

Frank Reno glowered at the uninvited guests. Singling out Allan Pinkerton, he sneered, "You might have gotten John, Mr. Bloodhound, but I'll fry in hell before you'll get the rest of us."

The Chief ignored the bandit. He had noticed that the stove was smoking suspiciously. "Bill," he said, "take a poker and yank off that lid."

Lifting the stove lid, Bill discovered bundles of tightly packed greenbacks. The fire was quickly doused and the money removed. Only a few bills were burned. Later this money was identified as that stolen in the Magnolia, Iowa, robbery.

The thieves were arrested and locked up in the Council Bluffs jail. Next evening the sheriff arrived at Allan Pinkerton's hotel with unpleasant news. Overnight the prisoners, evidently supplied from the outside with the proper tools, had knocked a hole in the side of the building and escaped. The note they left read: "APRIL FOOL."

Young Bill Pinkerton was furious. "Didn't that fool sheriff know better than to think a country jail could hold a man like Frank Reno without a round-the-clock guard?"

His father was more tolerant of human frailties. "Calm down, son," he said. "We'll get Frank Reno, one day or another."

Two months later, in an unusually well-planned robbery, an express was held up at Marshfield, Indiana, by a twelve-man gang. Close to $100,000 was taken from the Adams Express Company safes. The gang then split up. Frank Reno and four associates disappeared, and Simeon and William made for Indianapolis. The rest of the gang, led by desperado John Moore, stayed in the Marshfield area to plan a second train robbery.

At the request of Adams Express, Allan Pinkerton left Chicago for Indiana to take over investigation of the Marshfield theft.

On his second day in Marshfield an engineer named George Flanders called to see the detective chief at his hotel. Flanders said he had been approached by Moore to share in the robbery proceeds of the next train on his run that contained a large shipment of gold. Intending to play along with the thieves in order to assist in their capture, Flanders had agreed to the scheme. The next meeting of the gang was to be held at the Renos' hotel in Seymour.

"Fine," the Chief told the engineer. "We'll arrange for a big shipment of gold that doesn't exist. When the gang comes aboard they'll find more than gold bricks. And Moore is certain to lead us to the Renos."

Flanders' mouth dropped open. "Is this fellow Moore part of the Reno gang?"

"He must be. The Reno boys don't allow competitors to hold meetings at their hotel."

A week later, at the hotel, George Flanders told John Moore and his gang that a large shipment of gold, totaling almost $100,000, would be carried on the Jefferson, Missouri and Indianapolis Railroad on the night of July 10, 1868. The best place to rob the train was at a small fueling station near Shields, Indiana, a few miles west of Seymour. The gang was delighted with the size of the loot, and promised Flanders 25 per cent of it for his services.

The robbery went off as planned. John Moore entered the engine cab near Shields and tied up the unprotesting Flanders. The rest of the gang took a crowbar to the express car door and swiftly jimmied it open.

Inside Allan Pinkerton and four other operatives waited for them. As the last of the outlaws piled into the car the shooting began. Three of the six outlaws, including Moore, were wounded and captured; the other three fled, only to be caught within a few hours of the gun battle. None of the detectives suffered a scratch.

Though uninvited by Allan Pinkerton, local posses had assisted in the search for the escaped bandits. Now that the Reno gang was on the run, feeling against them in Seymour was high. The detectives wanted to avoid a lynching and sent the prisoners to Cincinnati for their safety.

A week after the robbery, three of Moore's men were returned to Shields for arraignment. They never arrived. Outside of Seymour a mob of almost two hundred night riders, wearing scarlet masks, flagged down the train. The Pinkerton men and Jackson County deputies were quickly disarmed, and their prisoners carried off into the woods. The hanging took less than five minutes.

Allan Pinkerton was livid with anger. Not only had the mob cheated justice, but the agency was guilty of turning over its prisoners to lynchers hiding behind masks. He would have fired the operatives who had been cowed by the Seymour mob had not George Bangs sent a telegram from Chicago interceding in their behalf.

Though law and order had been mocked, the Reno gang seemed broken—Seymour no longer feared them. As if the brothers themselves realized this, the gang disintegrated. William and Simeon Reno were captured rather easily in Indianapolis, and under questioning in Cincinnati, John Moore revealed the whereabouts of Frank Reno. The bandit leader had fled to Canada.

The detective chief persuaded the authorities in Windsor, Canada, to take Frank Reno into custody. He then asked Secretary of State Seward for extradition papers. Frank Reno fought for his freedom with every weapon at his command, including able lawyers and seemingly unlimited funds. While the preliminary hearings dragged on, the outlaw decided to eliminate his most dangerous enemy. Dick Barry, a Detroit burglar, was hired to assassinate Allan Pinkerton.

The attempt was made in early September on the Detroit ferry ramp. Barry made the mistake of taking time to aim carefully at his intended victim. The Chief, acting with lightning swiftness, grabbed Barry's revolver, handcuffed the would-be killer and delivered him to the Detroit police.

When Frank Reno heard the news in his Windsor cell, he angrily dashed his dinner to the floor.

Learning of the attempted assassination, Secretary Seward ordered a gunboat to the Canadian city. It stayed there for almost two weeks, and steamed off only after the Canadian government had lodged a protest.

Finally the Canadian authorities placed Reno and his three associates in the custody of Allan Pinkerton, Bill Pinkerton, and three agency operatives. Hobbled and handcuffed, the outlaws left Windsor in a seagoing tub bound for Detroit.

Frank Reno stared balefully at the stubborn adversary who had so relentlessly tracked him down.

"Pinkerton," he said, "I'm sorry Barry didn't get you in Detroit, but I've got a funny feeling you'll never see the town alive."

The detective smiled. "Maybe, Frank. But don't forget you're on this boat, too, and our next stop is Detroit."

It was then it happened. There was a sudden, rending crash, and the tug split in two. The detectives and their charges were catapulted into the water. By a miracle, none of the heavily ironed outlaws were drowned. Minutes later, as the tug sank alongside them, the soaked men were taken aboard the steamer that had rammed the smaller boat.

"Did you arrange that little accident, Frank?" the detective asked the bandit.

Reno grinned slyly. "Maybe I did, and maybe I didn't. But you'll never know."

Though the underworld had threatened Pinkerton with death if he ever removed Frank Reno from Canadian soil, the detective never believed the ramming of the tug was anything more than an accident, caused by a mistake in signals.

In Detroit the detectives and the outlaws changed their clothes and went aboard a steamer bound for Cleveland. During the trip Frank Reno jumped through a washroom window and had to be rescued from drowning a second time. It was Bill Pinkerton who did the honors.

The young detective was hauled aboard, dripping. He grinned at his father. "Dad, next time please make sure I bring along at least two changes of clothing."

From Cleveland the prisoners were taken to Louisville, Kentucky, and delivered the following day to the sheriff of Floyd County, Indiana. There they joined William and Simeon Reno in the New Albany jail. The Pinkertons went home.

Events moved swiftly. When the Reno henchmen heard that vigilantes in southern Indiana planned to attack the jailhouse and lynch the prisoners, they fought back with a calculated campaign of terror. Men suspected of being vigilante leaders were beaten and slashed; others were warned their children would be murdered if they dared take action against Frank Reno and his friends. The people of Floyd County barred their doors at night and moved behind lowered shades.

The Thanksgiving Day gathering of the family at Chicago that year was a subdued one; the men's thoughts were on New

Albany and the violence that might explode there any moment.

Allan had sent the governor of Indiana a telegram urging him to declare a state of martial law in Floyd County, but his advice was ignored.

"We've got to do something," said Bill. He looked around the table. "Any suggestions?"

"What about sending all our men to guard the jail?" asked Bob. The question was directed to his father.

Allan shook his head. "We can't go over the heads of the state authorities. The governor would have a right to arrest us, and he probably would."

Joan Pinkerton's turkey was getting cold, and Renos or no Renos, she was going to see that it was eaten hot.

"Allan," she said, "more gravy?"

There was no answer from her husband; he was still deep in thought.

She turned to William. "Bill, take another yam."

William, his brow furrowed in concentration, ignored her.

Joan rapped Bob on the knuckles. "Son, if you've finished your cider, there's plenty more on the sideboard."

Bob's mind was on New Albany. He gave no sign he had heard.

His mother looked to her daughter for understanding and commiseration, but Joanie only smiled and shrugged.

Joan Pinkerton had been driven to her limit. She sat back, drew a deep breath—and screamed.

For that day, at least, there was no more talk in the Pinkerton house about the Reno brothers and New Albany.

At midnight of December 11, a mob of over a thousand attacked New Albany prison. The sheriff telegraphed the governor for the militia and barricaded himself in the jail.

Frank Reno begged the sheriff to let his two younger

brothers make a break for it, but the lawman regretfully refused.

The mob stormed the jail. Though the sheriff and his deputies defended their prisoners as long as they could, the inevitable happened. The three Reno brothers and their associates in banditry were strung up from the jail rafters and hung there until they were dead.

As the man who had ended the careers of the most vicious desperadoes ever to terrorize the Midwest, Pinkerton received hundreds of letters and telegrams of congratulation. He read the first few that poured into the Chicago office, but threw the rest away.

To Allan Pinkerton the lynchings at New Albany were a crime more horrible than any the Renos had committed in their three years of outlawry. Violence, however much it deluded itself that its motives were good, was not justice, and never could be.

9 A Chicago Murder and a Brooklyn Manhunt

WHEN THE PINKERTON BROTHERS JOINED THE AGENCY AFTER their discharge from the Secret Service, their father typically decided that no favoritism was to be shown to his sons. They were to learn the business "from the ground up," and they did, Bill in Chicago and Bob in New York, under Superintendent Francis Warner.

For more than three years, uncomplainingly, the brothers did the more menial work of the agency, stamping letters, taking down wireless messages, running errands and making themselves generally useful while they looked, listened and—it was their father's hope—absorbed.

In the winter of 1869, Bob came home for Christmas. Having a few days of free time, he spent them working at the Chicago office.

On the night of December 18, 1869, Stanley Trafton, the son of a wealthy Cleveland merchant, was found dead in his bed in a Chicago rooming house. The coroner's verdict was death resulting from congestion of the lungs, and the police declared the case closed. True there was a flu epidemic at the time and many had died of lung congestion, but the circumstances were suspicious. Young Trafton's health had been excellent, and over two thousand dollars in bonds he had been carrying were unaccounted for. The dead man's father, who knew Allan Pinkerton, asked him to investigate.

Five minutes after the Chief had wired Trafton senior his acceptance, Bob and Bill presented themselves in his office.

"We want to work with you on the Trafton case," they told him.

"Think you've had enough experience to make yourself useful, eh?" their father said.

"Isn't it about time we tried?" asked Bob.

The Chief reached for his hat. "All right, I'm going over to the morgue to view the body. You come along."

At the morgue the Chief asked his sons if they noticed anything unusual.

Both examined the body and for good measure checked over young Trafton's clothes. They shook their heads in the negative.

The Chief picked up one of the young man's boots. "Look at this—whitewash across the sole, as if the lad's feet had been violently scraped across a wall."

"I didn't notice," Bill said, and Bob admitted he hadn't either.

"I'm going over to the rooming house and see how this whitewash got on Trafton's boot," the Chief told them. "You're welcome to come along."

The rooming house, at 92 West Madison Street, was run by a Mrs. May Pattmore, a strongly built woman in her forties. She greeted the detective and his two assistants pleasantly and showed them the room where Stanley Trafton had died. Though the Chief looked carefully along the walls for signs of any heavy scraping, there were none. The room had been recently whitewashed with a double coat of a heavy preparation.

"Did your handyman do this job of whitewashing?" the Chief asked Mrs. Pattmore casually.

"I did," replied the widow.

"Must have been quite a job. The two-gallon pails of whitewash they sell nowadays are pretty heavy."

The woman laughed. "Oh, I'm strong, Mr. Pinkerton. I've always prided myself on being able to do almost any job around the house a man can, and do it better."

The detective nodded absently. "Well, I guess that's all for today, Mrs. Pattmore. Thanks for your cooperation."

Outside, Allan Pinkerton turned to Bob. "Any thoughts or conclusions?"

"The fact that Mrs. Pattmore whitewashed the room so recently looks suspicious, when you tie it up with that whitewash on Trafton's boot," Bob said.

"And you, Bill?" the Chief asked William.

"I was thinking the same thing."

"Any other reactions?"

The two young men shook their heads.

Returning to his office, the Chief found waiting for him the telegraphed information on Mrs. Pattmore he had requested from an agent in Buffalo. May Pattmore had run a boardinghouse in that city for several years before coming to Chicago.

The information was decidedly unfavorable. Mrs. Pattmore was not a widow, but divorced from a husband who had disappeared under mysterious circumstances. On two occasions her boarders had had her arrested on suspicion of theft, although neither case had been proved against her in court.

Again the Chief asked his sons for suggestions.

"We've got enough on the woman to arrest her," Bill said.

"I agree," said Bob. "I'd haul her in for questioning and get her to say why she rewhitewashed Trafton's room."

"I'm afraid not," the Chief told them. "Unproved suspicion of theft, along with present evidence, wouldn't justify an arrest. We'd only leave ourselves wide open to false arrest charges."

Both boys reddened, and Bill asked, "Then what's your next move?"

"I'm going to have John Ingham take a room at Mrs. Pattmore's, representing himself as a bookmaker who left his last job in Louisville because of a shortage he couldn't explain. After gaining her confidence, he'll then suggest that he and May go into the business of robbing affluent strangers Ingham will steer to her house."

"Using the panel game?" asked Bob.

"Yes. Ingham will say he knows how to build a panel system by which any bedchamber in the house can be entered at will."

Pinkerton operative Ingham moved into the house on West Madison Street. He found May Pattmore more than willing to supplement her income by a life of crime. While sliding wall panels were being built in two of her rooms, Ingham pretended to look for wealthy strangers who were having difficulty finding a hotel room in Chicago. He came across a young man named Adamson, who was so naïve, Ingham told Mrs. Pattmore, that he freely displayed the ten fifty-dollar bonds he was carrying. Adamson, actually Robert Pinkerton disguised with a moustache and a limp, moved into the house on Madison Street the next day.

This attempt to trap May Pattmore unfortunately miscarried. On the night Ingham chose to "rob" Adamson the sliding panel stuck, and he was unable to gain entrance to his room. The next night, however, he followed Adamson out to an unlit section of town and "robbed" him there.

Ingham told Mrs. Pattmore he had been successful in taking his victim's bonds, and she immediately demanded her share. Bob Pinkerton, unfortunately, had misplaced them. When Ingham was unable to provide the bonds, she promptly turned him over to the police as Adamson's attacker. Since the story of Ingham's wholly imaginary attack on Adamson had been printed at Allan Pinkerton's request in *The Chicago Tribune,* the police had no recourse but to "arrest" him.

"Did you finally find the bonds, Bob?" Allan asked him gently.

"Yes, I'd left them at the office."

"Fed up with the case?"

"I'm still game," Bob said. "But how am I going to get back into it?" His voice had a plaintive note.

"As Robert Lacey," his father told him, "a rich Texan on the lookout for a good investment, who begins visiting Bill here at Mrs. Pattmore's. Bill's going to pose as a Yankee swindler who just arrived in Chicago. Living in the boarding-house, he'll also have a chance to search it for incriminating evidence."

"Won't the woman recognize me from that first visit?" asked Bill.

"She didn't recognize Bob as Adamson." The Chief cleared his throat. "As a matter of fact, I think May Pattmore's a little nearsighted."

The woman recognized neither Bill nor Bob, and offered Lacey some government bonds at a good price. The Texan insisted on seeing the merchandise before he bought it, and managed to memorize some of the serial numbers.

"I want to consult a banker friend of mine on the deal," Lacey said, and left for the agency on Washington Street. There the Chief compared the serial numbers Bob wrote down with those Trafton senior had sent him from Cleveland. They matched.

An hour later the Chief, accompanied by Bob, was shown into May Pattmore's parlor. When she saw Allan Pinkerton the widow went pale.

"Mrs. Pattmore," the Chief said, "I have a warrant for your arrest."

"The charge?" she demanded.

"Larceny."

May Pattmore visibly relaxed. But she was overconfident, for after searching the house, the Chief found not only most of the missing Trafton bonds, but a packet of morphine and a hypodermic in a vase that had been overlooked by Bill Pinkerton.

The Chief confronted her with this last piece of evidence. "Better confess, May. I'm warning you—you won't get another chance to use this stuff until you do."

May Pattmore admitted she had tried to drug and rob Stanley Trafton. The morphine she gave him in a glass of beer had seemed to work, but then he began to revive and she had panicked. She had broken a pitcher over his head, killing him instantly, and then, hoping to pretend Trafton had died in his sleep, dragged him into the bedroom and onto the bed. As the Chief suspected, she had rewhitewashed the bedroom in order to obliterate the telltale marks made by Trafton's boots as they scraped along the baseboard.

Bob and Bill admitted they could have done considerably better in their first case and confessed they needed more seasoning before tackling another. But the Chief smoothed their wounded feelings by complimenting Bob on his Texas accent and Bill on the false whiskers he had worn as the Yankee swindler.

The state was unable to produce evidence of premeditated murder, and May Pattmore went to prison for five years. But it might as well have been a death sentence. Behind bars and deprived of the morphine she could no longer do without, she went insane and was transferred to a state asylum. She died there a short time later.

In 1873 the Pennsylvania State Insurance Commission, made suspicious by the actions of the Central Fire Insurance Company of Philadelphia, ordered an examination of the company's assets. These were discovered to consist exclusively of forged certificates of Pennsylvania & Reading stock. In order to protect its stockholders from other such forgeries, the railroad retained Allan Pinkerton to hunt down the forger.

After questioning the insurance company president, Allan Pinkerton got him to admit that he had hired a Charles Ripley of New York to counterfeit the shares. The president insisted he had met Ripley only once, and described him sparsely as a "tall, bearded man." He had no current address for Ripley, beyond a saloon on Bridge Street in Brooklyn, New York.

"Do you think he's telling everything he knows?" Bill Pinkerton asked his father. "Could as big a job as this one have been accomplished after a single meeting?"

"Probably, if Canter's our man."

Bill's eyes went round. "Jack Canter?"

"Canter's well-known for quick deals, and he's the only first-rate counterfeiter in the East at the moment."

Bill's eyes glittered. "I always hoped we'd get a chance at old Jack."

Jack Canter was an amazing criminal, noted chiefly for his success in crime while behind bars. Now in his mid-forties, he had spent more than half his life in Sing Sing, yet had taught himself to be an expert linguist, penman, photographer, chemist, engraver and a passable amateur poet. At the Ossining, New York, prison he was given the job of prison bookkeeper, and made his work a means of building up a small personal fortune. Learning from the prison records which of the inmates had wealthy friends, he would, through an intermediary, approach those friends and offer a reduction in sentence in return for payment of a stiff fee. Since the warden never bothered to check the discharge book, Jack Canter could shorten the favored prisoners' terms at will.

For some reason or other, Canter never bothered to change his own records. Perhaps he saw no need to—conditions for him at Sing Sing were so lenient that he was permitted to spend weekends in New York, and the finest team of horses in Ossining was registered at the town livery stable in his name.

Checking with Sing Sing, Allan Pinkerton learned that Canter had been released about six months earlier. Word was that he had gone to San Francisco, but the detective knew better than that.

From Philadelphia the Chief went to New York and dropped in at the Brooklyn saloon to which the insurance company president had directed him. There he learned that letters written to Charles Ripley, in care of the saloon, were being picked up by a Mr. Charles Ostend. Ostend lived directly across the street from Brooklyn's third precinct police station.

The Chief grinned. If Jack Canter, alias Charles Ripley, alias Charles Ostend, couldn't make his home in a prison, a police station was the next best thing.

"What's this Ostend look like?" the detective asked the saloonkeeper.

"Never seen him," the man answered. "He sends a kid for his mail."

The detective's quarry lived in a rundown apartment building that had several entrances and exits. Ostend wasn't at home. Letting himself into the flat with a special key, Pinkerton searched the place thoroughly. There was no incriminating evidence, but Allan Pinkerton knew the counterfeiter must have hidden his tools of the trade somewhere around the apartment.

Leaving Canter's place, the Chief returned to his Brooklyn hotel and arranged for Bill Pinkerton and two operatives from the New York office to join him. Jack Canter would never be caught by one man.

The next day he returned to Canter's apartment. The counterfeiter was out again, but there was no doubt he had noted the detective's presence. Most of his clothes were gone, and a note sat propped up on the table. It read: "Hello, Pinkerton. I guess you missed me. I'll give you another chance to get Jack Canter when he comes back for the rest of his things."

For a week the Chief and his men watched Canter's apartment building, noting every individual who came in or out. Despite this round-the-clock surveillance, the rest of Canter's things disappeared from his flat. But some of the counterfeiter's valued books still remained, and the Chief was sure he would return for them.

At noon on the ninth day Bill Pinkerton, stationed at the back of the building, reported to his father on the persons who had entered it during the last hour.

"There was a porter—too short to be Canter—a delivery boy, and a chambermaid."

"How tall was the chambermaid?"

"Well, she seemed pretty big, but she was so stooped over I couldn't really tell. Dad, where are you off to?"

Allan Pinkerton had already started up the stairs. "Get the others!" he shouted over his shoulder. "Quick!"

A few seconds later the detective burst into Canter's flat. A tall woman stood before a secret panel in the wall which, open now, revealed a small nickel-plated press and a number of engravers' tools. The woman turned and grinned. "Hello, Pinkerton," she said in a deep voice, and slowly took off her wig.

It was Jack Canter, of course, and he confessed to the

forging of the P. & R. bonds, and was sentenced to ten years in prison. Unfortunately or otherwise, the authorities didn't see fit to return him to Sing Sing and his old life of comfort and influence. The daring counterfeiter was sent to the grim Eastern Penitentiary at Cherry Hill, Pennsylvania, known for its harsh treatment of prisoners.

In 1875 Pinkerton got a note from Jack Canter asking for a loan of one hundred dollars. He sent it, no questions asked. It was an action typical of the Chief; there were many loans and outright cash gifts to ex-antagonists outstanding on the agency books. Other men he had put behind bars came to him after serving their time, asking for help to rehabilitate themselves. He got jobs for some in banks and brokers' offices, watching for forgers and embezzlers; still others got good-paying positions with companies for whom the detective was doing work. Few ever failed the trust he had placed in them.

Nor, in his way, did Jack Canter. The hundred-dollar loan was never repaid, but in 1877 Pinkerton learned that Canter, seriously ill, had given the money to a cellmate whose child desperately needed an operation. The child recovered, but a few weeks later Jack Canter was dead.

10 A Pinkerton vs. the Molly Maguires

ALLAN PINKERTON HAD NO SOONER FINISHED WITH THE CANTER case than he was involved with another assignment that was to prove the most challenging of the agency's career. Like the Reno case, it involved clearing a section of a state from a gang of murderers and thieves who threatened the life of every decent citizen who dared to protest their lawless depredations. Unlike the Reno case, it meant coming to grips with a group of vicious gangsters operating in the guise of a benevolent brotherhood dedicated to "friendship, unity and true Christian charity."

In 1845 the Ancient Order of Hibernians was founded in Ireland, its purpose to fight the absentee landlords who were sucking the blood of Irish peasants and farmers. Soon criminals and men of dubious character invaded the organization, taking it over from men of more laudable aims, and used it for their own personal gain.

During the last six years, beginning in 1867, much the same thing had happened in the anthracite coal regions of Pennsylvania, where a secret society of Irish coal miners had been formed to fight for higher pay and better working conditions. This society was called the Mollies, or Molly Maguires, after the Hibernians' custom of wearing women's clothing as a disguise. Ruffians succeeded in gaining power

138

in the Mollies' central committee and, after expelling their respectable colleagues, took over as virtual dictators of the group.

Shrewdly they gathered around them a core of hardened loafers to whose advantage it was to see the criminal element of the group survive and wax strong. Ruthlessly these men extended their power to every county and township in the coal regions of Pennsylvania and formed local lodges commanded by "bodymasters" who were committed to a bloody code of violence against anyone—coal operator or maverick miner—who stood in their way.

The law found itself powerless against the Mollies. Local bodymasters sent for members of distant lodges to do their work of murder, kidnapping or arson, thus eliminating the possibility of identification. People knew that to inform against the Mollies meant death in the night, and even if witnesses could have been found to tell the truth, other "witnesses" stood in the Mollies' ranks ready to confound them with trumped-up or contradictory charges.

Franklin B. Gowen, president of the Philadelphia and Reading Railroad, had sympathy for the plight of the miner, who worked a twelve-hour day for eight dollars a week. But he knew the Mollies weren't the answer to that plight and asked Allan Pinkerton, then visiting the agency's Philadelphia branch, to come in for a talk. Gowen wanted to know if the detective believed he could successfully fight the Mollies and bring their leaders to justice. He was forced to admit that uniformed police and a number of detectives had already tried and failed.

"Can you give me a while, Mr. Gowen?" the detective asked. "Months, perhaps even a year or more?"

"I don't care how long it takes. Now how would you go about rooting out these killers?"

"My method would be to get a man inside the organization

where he could amass testimony that would destroy the leaders in court."

"Have you such a man in mind? Of course, he'd have to be an Irishman."

"Yes, Jimmy McParland. He's a son of Erin who came to Philadelphia in sixty-seven, and the brogue's still thick on his tongue. Jimmie's able, resourceful, intelligent and brave. Perhaps most important of all, he's got lots of charm. Everybody likes Jimmy."

"Sounds like you couldn't find a better man," commented Gowen. "Can you have this McParland in my office tomorrow morning?"

"I've got to ask him if he's game. This is dangerous work, and the odds are no better than even that he'll come back alive. If Jimmy refuses I can't blame him, but I think he'll want to try his hand at it."

In talking to Jimmy McParland, the Chief did not minimize the hazards involved in infiltrating the Mollies. He cited the score of murders they had already committed and noted their suspiciousness of outsiders. It would be no mean feat for McParland to be admitted to the organization, let alone gather the evidence that would incriminate them.

The slender, auburn-haired Irishman grinned. "I like to take chances, Mr. Pinkerton. I hope you won't be denyin' me the opportunity."

"Well, that settles it, Jimmy. You can leave tomorrow, after you buy some suitable clothes—and a cutty pipe."

McParland's mission was kept secret from all in the Philadelphia office except the superintendent, Benjamin Franklin. The Irishman's envious associates were told he was going abroad to England to track down a forger. Some smiled, but none openly questioned his story.

Dressed like a vagabond, the Irishman caught the noon train for Trenton, Pennsylvania, in late October, 1873. With him was a battered valise in which he carried a large supply of envelopes, writing paper and stamps. It was via the mails that McParland—under the name of James McKenna— planned to keep in touch with Allan Pinkerton in Chicago and Ben Franklin in Philadelphia. For an unemployed man looking for work in the mines, the telegraph would be too expensive—and eyebrow-raising—a means of communication.

In Trenton, McParland encountered a number of Irish, but he heard no open talk of the Molly McGuires. The conversation was all President Grant, and how he seemed unable to cope with steadily worsening business conditions.

For the next week McParland wandered around the towns nearby, accustoming himself to the country and its people and turning conversation to the Mollies whenever he could.

In Minerville his luck changed. There he met an Irishman named Dormer, who took immediately to the tramp with the fine singing voice. The fact that James McKenna was currently supplied with funds from his "war pension" did him no harm, since he was able to buy drinks freely. He represented himself as a "son of the ould sod" who had been mining in Colorado, and as a typical member of his race he was devil-may-care, tippling and reckless. He also claimed to be a member of Ireland's Ancient Order of Hibernians.

When McParland pressed Dormer to find him some work, his new friend said he could give him a letter to Muff Lawler.

"Muff's bodymaster of the Mollies in Shenandoah," Dormer said. "If he can't find you work, Jamie, there's no one who can."

In a letter to Allan Pinkerton in mid-November, McParland was able to tell him that he had established contact with a ranking member of the Mollies.

Before looking up Lawler, McParland dropped into a Shenandoah saloon. There he met a man named Durkin. As an Ancient Hibernian, Durkin said, McParland should make it his business to meet Jack Kehoe, who was County Delegate and high up in the local Mollies. Kehoe ran another saloon in town, the Hibernian House.

The meeting with Kehoe was disappointing. The sharp-eyed County Delegate was no fool. He seemed unimpressed with McParland's claim that he had killed a man in Buffalo, and when the agent failed to respond to a secret sign, he commented, "You don't seem much of an Erin man to me." McParland mumbled, "It's a very long time since I was within," and left the saloon.

The letter to Muff Lawler brought better results. Lawler took a shine to the newcomer, and not only promised to get him work in the mines, but asked McParland to board at his house.

"I sleep two to a bed with a miner who hasn't washed since last Christmas," McParland wrote his Chief. "But living with Lawler has its advantages. Yesterday Muff asked me to write a letter, since he doesn't know how, and suggested I could make ink with the family laundry bluing. From now on I won't be lacking for the stuff. However, could you please send me a supply of stamps, as it would be conspicuous if I made too many calls at the post office."

It was some time before Lawler got McParland a job, but the operative spent the time profitably by ingratiating himself with the local men. He bought drinks in the Shenandoah saloons, and told funny stories, and soon Jamie McKenna was a very popular young man. When someone asked how he happened to have so much ready money, McParland answered that he occasionally made a boodle in counterfeiting. His stock rose still higher.

Toward the end of January the job Lawler had promised him came through. It was loading coal, for ten hours a day, six days a week. When McParland's hands were hurt in an accident and he was laid off without compensation, he wrote

Allan Pinkerton that he was beginning to hate the mine-owners as well as any Molly. "If a mine boss in Girardville hadn't been murdered by Mollies just a couple of days ago, I well might have left you to go over to the other side."

But McParland's wavering was only temporary. When he heard that Lawler had proposed his name for membership in the Mollies, all his pride in a job well done returned. It was with a real feeling of triumph that he learned the Shenandoah Mollies had voted to admit him to their lodge. That night the spy bent his knee to take the Mollies' oath, made the sign of the cross and paid the treasurer a three-dollar initiation fee.

"The first real victory is won at last," he wrote the Chief, and added details of the beating of a Welsh mine boss in nearby Ferndale who had been left for dead by his Molly attackers.

The months passed. There was little or no work available at the mines, and McParland needed another explanation for the money in his pocket. He also needed an excuse for a meeting in Philadelphia with Allan Pinkerton.

"I've got to go to Scranton to get a job from my counterfeiting friends," he told Lawler. "Otherwise I'll be dead broke in a fortnight."

Lawler nodded. "You can deliver some messages for us to the Scranton body."

McParland delivered the messages in Scranton and went on to Philadelphia, where he and Pinkerton met at a Broad Street hotel.

The Chief was pleased with the written information McParland turned over to him. "You've certainly made fine progress, Jim, but I don't like the way you look. Tired and rundown."

McParland shrugged. "It's the terrible food and living

conditions, and the constant strain. At any moment the Mollies might unmask me."

"No job's worth the grave, Jimmy. Do you want to give it up?"

"No, sir," the operative said decisively. "If I've gone this far, I can go the rest of the distance. A McParland doesn't quit."

There were no questions asked when McParland returned to Shenandoah. Muff Lawler was too busy fighting for his position as bodymaster. During Jimmy's absence the Shenandoah lodge had voted to assassinate Gomer Jones, a local mine boss, and Lawler had overruled them. A faction of the lodge wanted to depose Lawler for his timidity and put another Molly in his place.

"They're talking of electing you bodymaster, Jamie," Lawler told McFarland. "They say you're a man of action."

"Lord, Muff, I wouldn't want that," McParland said truthfully.

Lawler eyed his boarder with a certain amount of jealous suspicion. "Well, then, you'd better tell the boys how you feel."

It was "McKenna for Bodymaster" in all the local saloons, and even Jack Kehoe was said to look upon his candidacy with favor. For a week McParland talked and argued his way out of a post that would have brought disaster: as bodymaster he would have been expected to carry out the murder not only of Gomer Jones but others as well. Finally the reluctant candidate went to see the influential Kehoe.

"MacAndrew's a better man for the job than myself," McParland told the County Delegate. "The boys keep forgetting that murder charge in Buffalo I've got hanging over my head. It wouldn't help for me to suddenly become known about the state."

"That's true enough," agreed Kehoe. "What about becoming lodge secretary? You can read and write, which is more than can be said for most of us."

"I wouldn't mind being secretary," McParland told him, trying not to show his excitement. As secretary of the Shenandoah lodge he would be in charge of all its records, and privy to its correspondence with other lodges throughout the state.

"Well, I'll put in a good word for you," Kehoe said, and winked.

MacAndrew was elected bodymaster and McParland secretary. That night the spy wrote his Chief in Chicago: "I would advise that you arrange for the Philadelphia office to persuade Gomer Jones to leave the neighborhood. As things now stand, he will be murdered any day."

Superintendent Franklin's efforts to get Jones to leave Shenandoah were a failure. The stubborn Welshman refused to give ground. At considerable risk to himself, McParland called on him to add his warning.

"These Mollies are cowards," the mine boss insisted. "The worse they'll do is rough me up again."

Bodymaster MacAndrew proved as timid an executioner as had Muff Lawler, and the rank and file grew impatient to have Jones' murder over and done with. To the consternation of McParland, Jack Kehoe approached him to do the job. McParland could only remind the leader that he was wanted for murder in New York State.

"That's why I'm here to talk you into it," snapped Kehoe. "You're the only man with any guts in this lodge."

"Give me a chance to think it over, Jack," McParland said. That night he wrote Allan Pinkerton again, asking for advice. The Chief replied: "There's only one thing to do. Start drinking so heavily that Kehoe is convinced you're untrustworthy."

The ruse worked, but at the same time Kehoe lost respect for McParland, and on more than one occasion, the spy noticed the County Delegate watching him with a strange look in his eye.

On a cold night in March, 1874, Gomer Jones was shot down by two men. It was Kehoe's work; McParland and Mac-Andrew hadn't even been consulted about the assassination. MacAndrew resigned his position as bodymaster, and a Kehoe man, Bridey, was put in his place.

"Do you want my resignation, too?" McParland asked Kehoe. "It isn't as if I've been very much help to you lately."

"You keep good records, McKenna," the Irishman grunted. "Don't think of quitting till I give you the word."

"Who did the Jones killing, Jack?" McParland asked, as if only mildly interested.

"Hurley and McLaughlin," Kehoe answered. "I want you to give them a reward out of lodge funds."

In the next weeks new shutdowns at the mines put mine workers and Mollies into ugly moods. There were constant brawls between Welsh and Irish, and in April six victims were murdered in Schuylkill and Columbia counties. Had it not been for Jimmy McParland, double that number would have died. He did all he could to get warnings through to those marked down for execution, often risking exposure by appearing in person at their homes. Some listened; some, like Gomer Jones, did not. McParland was successful in getting advance word to Superintendent Franklin about Molly plans to blow up bridges essential to the mine operators in shipping their coal. Three such acts of sabotage were prevented when guards of the Coal and Iron Police, the mineowners' private police force, were posted at the bridges involved.

As usual, Allan Pinkerton received information on the killings in the form of detailed reports sent to him from Shenandoah.

In late April, McParland met at a Philadelphia hotel with

Allan Pinkerton, Superintendent Franklin and Robert Linden, Pinkerton assistant superintendent in Chicago.

"Jim," the Chief told him, "we're adding a dozen of our men to the Coal and Iron Police. One of them is going to be Bob Linden here. He'll walk up to you at the Hibernian House and greet you as an old acquaintance from Buffalo. Later you'll be able to be seen talking to him without too much suspicion."

Linden came up to McParland at the Hibernian House with Jack Kehoe looking on. Jamie McKenna was so popular that his peers saw nothing strange in a policeman striking up reacquaintance with him. Thereafter McParland met Linden often at Kehoe's and elsewhere and passed him a number of messages and notes. One of them concerned the killers of two policemen of Tamaqua, a nearby town.

As things turned out, this identification was crucial in the fight against the Mollies. The alleged killers McParland had named were arrested, and one of them, ignorant that the only evidence against him was McParland's hearsay information, confessed. He and his partner were promptly indicted for the murders.

The Mollies reeled from the blow. A more serious one befell them a few weeks later, when a complete list of all the members of the brotherhood was released by Allan Pinkerton to the newspapers of the nation. This could mean only one thing—a spy in the Mollies' inside councils.

A special meeting of Molly officials was called in Wilkes-Barre. James McParland was one of the few not invited to attend. There was no time to write for help, and McParland wired Franklin in Philadelphia. "I am surely suspected," the message went. "Unless you arrest me immediately, or cause the local authorities to arrest me, I am lost."

Superintendent Franklin never received the wire, which miscarried.

The next morning McParland looked out his window to see Molly guards stationed around the rooming house. He was sure he was a doomed man.

MacAndrew, who had attended the Wilkes-Barre meeting, came to see him after breakfast.

"So they've decided I'm the spy?" McParland asked the ex-bodymaster.

"They're not sure. Kehoe's called a meeting of county bodymasters in Shenandoah for tomorrow night. They'll give you a fair trial then."

McParland licked his lips. "Do you know what evidence they're holding against me?"

"Someone saw you in Philadelphia meeting a man on the sly, in a hotel, and a lot of writing paper was found in your suitcase. Postmaster Leary says you're always mailing letters. Then there's the question of your money. Nobody believes you made it by counterfeiting."

"Do you, Bob?" McParland asked him quietly.

"I don't care how you made it. I'm your friend, and I'm here to help you."

"Then come with me to Kehoe's. I mean to have this out with him now."

The guards didn't stop McParland, but they insisted on tagging along. The spy hired a sleigh at the livery stable, and the four men set off for Kehoe's house, some three miles away.

McParland broke into the County Delegate's house shouting, "I hear ye want me life, Kehoe, and I'm here to ask you the why of it!"

Kehoe's eyes were deadly, but his tone was mild. "Your trial is set for tonight, McKenna, if that's your name. Till then there's no sense in discussing the matter."

"That Postmaster Leary's a liar!" McParland yelled. "I'll bring him back here and prove it to you."

Kehoe shrugged, and returned to the game of cards he was playing with some cronies. McParland left the house, followed by MacAndrew and the guards, who had managed to down a few drinks at Kehoe's sideboard and were quite gay. They piled into the sleigh, and the driver headed for the postmaster's house; but when they arrived there, they learned that Mr. Leary had gone to Tamaqua to see his married daughter.

"To the railroad station," McParland ordered the driver. "I'm going to wire Leary to come back."

At the station McParland asked for a telegraph blank, and began to ponder a message. Meanwhile he kept his eye peeled for the Scranton local, due momentarily at the Shenandoah stop.

"Ain't you got that telegram writ yet?" one of the guards asked impatiently.

McParland balled up the yellow sheet and began again. "Just can't seem to get the right words," he said apologetically.

The Scranton local puffed into the station and Shenandoah passengers got aboard. There was a warning whistle from the cab, and then the screech of released hand brakes. McParland wheeled, pushed past the surprised guards and sprinted for the train. The guards rushed after him, tugging for their revolvers as McParland leapt for one of the vestibule platforms.

Several people were standing on the station platform and a woman screamed in fright. Cursing, one of the guards struck down his companion's weapon. "Can't you see he's flown the coop, Ed? Put your gun away, or it's jail for both of us."

The other man groaned, looking after the disappearing train. "The saints preserve us! What'll Jack Kehoe say now?"

With McParland's safe return to Philadelphia, warrants

were drawn up for the arrest of the Mollies' ringleaders and hired killers. In a few weeks most of them were behind bars, and the police of three states were hunting for others.

Their trials received nationwide attention. McParland's evidence against them, together with that provided by a number of Mollies who turned state's evidence, was more than enough to result in the conviction of more than thirty-five members of the brotherhood, Jack Kehoe among them. Several were found guilty of murder, others received only minor sentences. Some were acquitted, among them MacAndrew, of whom McParland spoke well in court.

The power of the Molly Maguires in the coal mines and towns of Pennsylvania was broken forever.

Jimmy McParland's thirteen-month ordeal left him broken in health, and he accepted Allan Pinkerton's invitation to the country house the Chief had just completed at Onarga, Iroquois County, Illinois. He was there for over six months in hiding from possible Molly vengeance. McParland spent much of his time with Isabella Pinkerton, now an old lady, whom her successful son had brought over from Scotland to live out her last days in comfort. He came out only at night, when he and the Chief took brisk walks. When he was partly recovered, Jimmy McParland moved from Philadelphia to the gentler climate of Colorado, where he eventually rose to be Superintendent of the Pinkerton office in Denver.

11 Baron Max and Handsome Walter

DURING HIS THIRTY-YEAR CAREER, THERE WAS ONLY ONE MAJOR criminal, with the exception of Jesse James, who escaped the long arm and eagle eye of Allan Pinkerton. He was Max Shinburn, alias Maximilian Schoenbein, alias Baron Shindle.

Shinburn was an example of the detective's axiom that many criminals, had they devoted themselves to earning an honest living, would undoubtedly have become honorable, even honored, members of society. Like Jack Canter, Max Shinburn was an intelligent and cultivated man. A college graduate, he spoke five languages, was widely read, and could hold his own with scholars in several fields. Like Canter, he found a normal existence unbearably tame, and demanded the excitement of a life dedicated to flouting authority and the conventions. An accomplished bank robber, he took great delight in choosing a financial institution that had boasted it was impregnable, and then robbing it of a record sum.

After leaving school in 1847, Shinburn went to work as a teller for a New York City bank. One day his books showed a shortage of one thousand dollars. The teller covered his tracks too cleverly for any charges to be preferred against him, but he was asked to resign.

Resolving to become a professional criminal, Shinburn set off for Boston. There he registered as Mr. Walker Watterson at the fashionable Revere House, and soon became known as an elegant bon vivant who had what appeared to be unlimited funds. Actually Shinburn was running low on money when he achieved the first of his objectives, the friendship of a wealthy Boston girl, the daughter of a distinguished banker. Shinburn became an intimate at her father's home, and was invited to "take a look around the City National." The old gentleman was later to regret the detailed answers he gave to Walker Watterson's many questions about the bank's vault system.

One night, after leaving a party at the banker's home, Shinburn paid another visit to the City National. He forced an entrance through a skylight, and immediately set to work on the vault lock. After an hour or so the safe swung open. Instead of taking a large sum of money, which would have led to new security precautions, he stole only a few thousand dollars. Then he made a wax impression of the vault lock and returned to his hotel.

The stolen money enabled Shinburn to continue his gilded life in Boston. Part of it he spent on the purchase of a Lillie safe, then known as the best made. He studied the safe's workings until he could open it blindfolded and, experimenting on his own, developed a delicate ratchet by which he could determine the combination of any Lillie safe, provided he was able to study its main lock unobserved for a short period of time.

A few weeks later Shinburn returned to the City National and took an additional $30,000. This was the last Boston saw of the elegant bank robber, who then set off on a tour of the New England states. In three years he took hundreds of thousands of dollars from banks in Connecticut, Rhode Island and Vermont. But in 1864 a confederate was captured and informed on the master thief, and Shinburn was arrested at New York's fashionable Saratoga spa.

The gates of the Concord, New Hampshire, prison closed behind him. But not for long. With incredible patience Shinburn contrived to take an impression of his cell lock with mashed potatoes, and then from an iron spoon, shaped a key to fit it. With a steel saw smuggled to him by a friend, he next sawed the bars of the corridor gate so that they would give at the right amount of pressure.

One evening while the guards were celebrating the birthday of a colleague, Shinburn opened his cell door with the spoon key, walked through the corridor door and jumped into a wagon waiting for him outside. Concord never saw him again.

On the night of July 9, 1868, the vault of the Lehigh Coal and Navigation Company, at White Haven, Pennsylvania, was opened by means of false keys. $57,000 was stolen. The president of Lehigh called in Allan Pinkerton, and was amazed by his certainty that Max Shinburn had masterminded the robbery.

"How can you be so sure?" he asked the detective.

"Mr. Braddock," the Chief answered, "after all these years of detective work I can almost immediately determine the character of a particular crime. Since I know the names, histories, habits and often the hideouts of men skilled in various kinds of crime, it isn't extraordinary for me to be able to put my finger on the guilty party and determine what disposition he is likely to make of his loot. Now there's no doubt at all that Max Shinburn is behind the White Haven theft. No other man opens a Lillie safe quite the way he does. I'm equally certain that he had confederates, amateurs, associated in some way with your company. My first move is to go to White Haven and ask some questions."

Under the Chief's relentless interrogation, Joseph Stark, proprietor of the White Haven Hotel, admitted that an elegant gentleman answering Shinburn's description, but called Sinclair, had been a guest at his hotel at the time of the robbery. Stark finally confessed that he had introduced this Mr. Sinclair to a Lehigh Company clerk named Wilson, and received a hundred-dollar bill for his pains.

Wilson was no match for the Chief's wily threats. He broke down and confessed his part in the robbery, which had amounted to giving Mr. Sinclair duplicates of the office keys and notifying him of the arrival at White Haven of the $57,000 in Lehigh Coal and Navigation funds.

"Where's Sinclair now?" the Chief asked the clerk.

"I'd tell you if I wasn't afraid he'd escape and come back and kill me," Wilson answered.

The Chief laughed. "Kill you? Why Max Shinburn wouldn't crush an ant. Didn't you know about his menagerie at Concord prison? He collected every stray cat and dog in the area. Finally the authorities had to build a shed to house them."

Wilson nodded. "I can believe that. He was always petting my German Shepherd and telling me I didn't feed him right."

"Well?"

"Shinburn's in Wilkes-Barre," Wilson confessed. "At the Bel-Mar Hotel."

Pinkerton arrested Shinburn in Wilkes-Barre without trouble, and the Chief was ready to turn him over to the police. The Lehigh Company, however, was reluctant to do so until Shinburn told them where the loot was hidden.

"My job was to arrest him," the detective objected. "In any case Shinburn will never talk. Moreover, you run the risk of his escaping."

Lehigh officials refused to listen, and Pinkerton's attempts to learn the whereabouts of the hidden money were unsuccessful. Giving up for the night, he left Shinburn in a room at the Wilkes-Barre Hotel in the custody of two operatives.

To insure against any possibility of his escape, Shinburn was handcuffed to one of them.

"I enjoyed my conversation," Shinburn called out jovially to the departing Chief, "but don't expect to resume it tomorrow. I have important business elsewhere."

Early the next morning Allan Pinkerton, in his second-floor room at the Wilkes-Barre, was awakened by a loud knocking at his door. The two operatives detailed to watch Max Shinburn stood there crestfallen, unable to meet his eye. From the wrist of one dangled a pair of handcuffs.

"I—I'm sorry, Chief," he stammered. "Shinburn got away."

"That's obvious," snapped the Chief. "How do you think he managed it?"

"I don't know, sir."

Contemptuously the Chief marched off to the room where the master criminal had been held prisoner. He found a pearl tie pin on the bed, and held it up for his embarrassed operatives' inspection.

"Smith," he demanded, "does this belong to you?"

The operative looked down at his tie, then nodded.

"Shinburn used your tie pin, Smith," the Chief said, "and while you slept, he picked the handcuffs. With his *left* hand. Then, Carson," he turned to glare at the other operative, "he tiptoed past your heavily sleeping form to the door. Handcuffed, with two men to guard him, and he got away!"

"We'll catch him, Chief," Smith assured him. "Wilkes-Barre isn't that big a town."

"I doubt it," the Chief answered, "but if you do, you can keep your job."

Three months later Allan Pinkerton learned Shinburn was in Belgium, which had no treaty of extradition with the United States. Smith resigned his position, but the Chief was generous enough to reinstate him.

In late June of the next year the Ocean National Bank

of New York City was robbed of nearly a million dollars, and the Chief knew that Max Shinburn had returned to the United States.

It was the most daring crime of the decade. Shinburn and his colleagues broke through the floor of the bank from the basement, hung black silk over the doors and windows and set to work. The master criminal apparently knew the vault's main combination and opened it easily. With a large jackscrew he opened smaller safes and locked compartments within the vault. The thieves left behind $25,000 in gold because it was too heavy to carry. They also abandoned an elaborate set of burglar tools worth $3000. The entire operation, begun on a Sunday morning, took less than twenty-four hours.

The Ocean National Bank remembered that Allan Pinkerton had warned them, in his regular monthly circular sent to banks all over the country, that criminal techniques were catching up with the particular vault system used at Ocean National. It asked the agency's New York branch to take the case on condition that Pinkerton senior head the investigation.

The Chief wired his New York superintendent to refuse. In a follow-up letter he explained his decision: "So perfectly planned a crime must include a perfect getaway. Shinburn will never be captured now, and believing this as I do, we would be taking money from a client under false pretenses. My decision has nothing to do with the fact that I have suffered a slight paralytic stroke. The only effect of this is a slight dragging of the left leg, and if I cannot run as fast as I used to do, my mind works as well as ever."

Max Shinburn did make the perfect getaway—back to Europe, where he bought a patent of nobility and settled down in a Belgian castle as Baron Shindle. Thereafter he turned both honest and philanthropic, and was never questioned or troubled by the Continental police again.

His reformation was no surprise to Allan Pinkerton. "Max always wanted to be a real gentleman," the detective said, when he heard from a European agent that the Baron had contributed $50,000 to a local charity. "A real gentleman lives quietly, and the only time he gets his name in the papers is when he gives away his money or when the years catch up with him for good."

But the Shinburn case did have one useful result. For a decade now Allan Pinkerton, successful in persuading a number of states to observe extradition proceedings for wanted criminals, had been working and lobbying for a system of extradition between the United States and other nations. His detectives had brought back criminals from Africa, Asia, Europe and even the South Seas, but this had been despite, not because of, sensible international agreements on hunted men. It was Max Shinburn's escape that made Washington legislators listen to the Chief, and within a short time the U. S. government signed extradition treaties with several foreign governments which effectively extended the arm of American law enforcement overseas. No longer could an American criminal find haven in Europe merely by setting foot on a foreign shore.

If Max Shinburn was the ablest criminal Allan Pinkerton ever encountered, Walter Sheridan was the most prepossessing. Sheridan, a tall blond with gray eyes, was as good to look at as Harry Montague, the day's greatest matinee idol.

Sheridan began his criminal career in St. Louis in 1858. While awaiting sentence for stealing a horse, he broke jail and escaped to Chicago.

There he fell in with Joe Moran, a hotel thief, and the two continued in partnership for nearly three years. In 1861, caught robbing a guest room at the Adams House, they were sentenced to a short term at the Illinois Penitentiary.

Released, Sheridan returned alone to Chicago, where he upped his sights and fell in with a gang of bank sneaks, becoming leader of the group. Bank sneaks used a variety of clever techniques to part careless tellers and depositors from their money. Sheridan and his partners worked the game in Cincinnati, St. Louis and other large cities until 1865, when Sheridan took still another step up the ladder and joined forces with George Williams, alias English George, one of the most aristocratic of bank robbers. Two years later, in 1867, Sheridan was worth over $100,000.

In Louisville, Kentucky, he and his gang took over $300,-000 from the Falls City Tobacco Bank. Patterning his approach after Shinburn's great Ocean National robbery, Sheridan and his crew rented an office below the bank vault. They then sawed through the floor directly into it. Lookouts were posted in a room over a restaurant directly opposite the bank. Despite unremitting effort by Louisville Police Department detectives, not a cent of the stolen money was recovered.

Eventually arrested in Ohio, Sheridan found himself sitting in Allan Pinkerton's private office, waiting for the Chief. Bill Pinkerton, guarding the prisoner, left him alone for a moment, and in his absence the wily Sheridan picked up the snuffbox on Allan's desk. Doubtless he planned to blind Bill with its contents, seize his revolver and make his escape. But Bill, gifted with his father's sixth sense, re-entered the room with a drawn revolver.

Taking a pinch of snuff, Sheridan returned the box to the desk and said, "Billy, this snuff of Allan's is great stuff."

"For the eyes, Walter?" Bill was quick to add.

"Eyes or nose," Sheridan replied. "But I'm very sorry to say that this time the *nos* have it!"

A bribed jury found Walter Sheridan not guilty, and he next organized the greatest series of forgeries in the criminal history of the United States. Forged bonds, to the value of five million dollars, were issued on seven American corporations. One of these was the Buffalo and Erie Railroad. Execution of the bonds was so faultless that when some of them were brought to Edgar Harley, president of the B. & E., that gentleman immediately bought $20,000 worth for his personal account.

In time he discovered the fraud and asked Allan Pinkerton to track down the forger before he could dispose of more of the counterfeit securities. The Chief was pessimistic. "We'll get Sheridan yet," he told Harley, "but at the moment we have absolutely no information on Handsome Walter or any of his associates. He's covered his tracks too well."

Harley was unaccustomed to such frankness. He raged, "Well, if you can't catch Sheridan, Pinkerton, I'll hire a detective who will!"

The Chief reached for his hat. "Oh, you'll find detectives who'll promise you the moon, Mr. Harley, but coming back with it, that's a different story."

Detectives hired by the B. & E. were unable to find Walter Sheridan. After they had given up the chase, Allan Pinkerton wrote Harley that his son had dined with Sheridan in Brussels. "Sheridan told my son, over pâté de fois gras, that he had been able to sell only two million dollars worth of bonds, of which two hundred thousand was in Buffalo and Erie shares. So I suppose you can be mildly grateful for that."

In reply Harley furiously criticized the detective for admitting that a Pinkerton operative, and his own son at that, openly associated with a criminal.

The detective answered: "You, my dear sir, fail to realize that there is no closer relationship than that between two natural enemies, who spend most of their time thinking only of how to destroy each other."

One piece of information Bill Pinkerton took away from

his expensive dinner with Walter Sheridan was that the bank robber and forger intended to return to America. Sheridan had insisted, once too often, that he planned to remain in Belgium.

Walter Sheridan did return to the United States, and went into the florist business in Denver, Colorado, under the name of David Stewart. He was immediately successful, and within a few years, in 1871, was a director of a Denver bank. He even established a bank of his own in a mining area of the state. But his gambling instinct led him astray, and after speculating wildly in mining stock, he lost almost every dollar he had.

The Pinkerton branch in Denver had been watching Stewart, and reported to the Chief on this gambling man who so much resembled Walter Sheridan, except for the long sideburns he affected.

The Chief asked Bob Pinkerton to go out to Denver and see what he could make of the suspect. If Stewart decided to take a trip, he was to follow him.

Stewart was Sheridan without a doubt, Bob wired his father. He had also learned that Stewart planned to make a trip to New York to consult doctors about his failing health.

"Sheridan has eighty-two indictments hanging over his head in New York City," the Chief wired back. "Arrest him there. A bench warrant will be waiting for you at Church Street Police Station."

As Walter Sheridan stepped from the Pennsylvania Railroad ferryboat onto New York City soil at the foot of Desbrosses Street, Bob Pinkerton slipped his arm through his.

"Sheridan," he said, "it's all over. I have a bench warrant in my pocket."

The fugitive's shoulders sagged. He didn't even ask to see the warrant. "All right," he said softly. "I guess I knew the game was up."

Sheridan's bad health made the jury sympathetic toward him, and he was shrewd enough to appear in clothes so ragged that even his attorney had difficulty recognizing his own client. A number of witnesses had the same problem, and Handsome Walter received a brief five-year sentence.

Bob Pinkerton was indignant. "Only five years, and with all those indictments against him!"

"Have a little charity, son," the Chief told him. "If Walter Sheridan lives another five years he'll be lucky."

The bank robber and forger died two years later, in 1873. Allan Pinkerton, then on business in New York, attended his funeral, the only mourner except for two fashionable young women, both heavily veiled and dressed in black.

Neither gave the slightest indication she knew the other existed, and when Handsome Walter was laid to rest, each, weeping bitterly, left the cemetery by a separate exit.

12 Jesse James

On the afternoon of April 12, 1874, Pinkerton detective John Whicher was called to the Chief's office. Waiting for him there were Allan and Bill Pinkerton.

The Chief opened the discussion. "John, have you read the file on Frank and Jesse James?"

The tall, fair-haired Whicher nodded and grinned. "I memorized it, Chief. There isn't anything we have on Frank and Jesse I can't quote you chapter and verse. Except," he paused significantly, "what they look like."

Father and son exchanged glances and Bill said, "Sorry we can't help you there, John. That's one big reason why the Jameses are still at large. Nobody's ever been able to take a picture of them."

Allan Pinkerton shifted in his chair. "John, suppose you give us back a little of that information. We want to be satisfied you're armed with all the facts. Facts can save a man's life if they're used right, and in any case they're all we've got to go on. One Pinkerton's already died under the James gang's guns. We want you back from this assignment alive."

Whicher launched into his chapter and verse. He talked for half an hour, and more than once the Chief poured him fresh water from the carafe on his rolltop desk. Though

162

almost as familiar with the James file as Whicher, the Pinkertons sat spellbound. From his recital of facts, dates, persons and places, the James legend clearly emerged in all its color and drama, its violence and fury. The Pinkertons were professionals whose business it was to track down criminals without sentiment and without fuss; professionals who, over the years, had become little disposed to glamorize their opponents. Yet, as Whicher went on, they proved no less immune to the lure of Jesse James—hero, bandit and killer—than other men. Bill Pinkerton smiled thoughtfully and his eyes had a faraway look. The expression on his father's lined face —he was fifty-five now—was much the same.

John Whicher told them that the James boys came of good pioneer Kentucky stock. Frank, the firstborn, had seen the light of day in January, 1844. Jesse was born three years later. The boys' father, Robert James, was a Baptist minister with a good education; their mother, a strong-willed woman, was a vigorous worker in the church. Robert James owned and worked a farm near Kearny, Clay County, Missouri. When times got bad and the gold rush in California beckoned, he left for the Golden State, and died there. His wife remained a widow for four years, and in 1855 married Dr. Reuben Samuels.

With the coming of the Civil War, many Abolitionist Jayhawker bands made the conflict an excuse for pillage and robbery. Clay and Jackson counties were settled mostly by people with southern sympathies, many of them from Kentucky. Jayhawkers from Kansas stole and drove off horses and cattle, burned houses and hanged men. These outrages led to the organization of the Missouri guerrillas under William Clarke Quantrell, a southern patriot-brigand who had devoted his life to revenge against the Jayhawkers because they had murdered his brother.

In 1862 Frank James, who enjoyed quoting from the Bible

and Shakespeare, joined Quantrell's ranks. A year later a Jayhawker band, searching for the guerrilla leader, tortured Dr. Samuels and jabbed fifteen-year-old Jesse with bayonets. That was enough to get Jesse to join up with Quantrell. In skirmishes and ambushes on the Kansas-Missouri border, the baby-faced lad fought bravely and brilliantly against Federal troops. Quantrell described him as his best soldier. In May, 1865, Jesse surrendered his force to a Union regiment. Frank James surrendered with the main body of Quantrell's troops three months later.

Though war had ended, the old hatreds between pro- and anti-slavers festered in the Missouri-Kansas border country. Nearly two years after Appomattox, Frank and Jesse were still being harried by Federal sympathizers who could not forget they had ridden with the dreaded Quantrell. Once militiamen attacked the Samuels homestead in Kearny, and Jesse fought them off with a revolver in each hand. Finally the brothers were forced to go into hiding, and their travels took them to New York, Panama and California.

They returned to Missouri, but the old feuds still smouldered, and they found it hard to readjust. Then, to make things still worse, the state of Missouri adopted a bill stipulating that all ex-Confederate soldiers were forbidden to practice a profession.

Jesse and Frank refused to be driven from Clay County, their homeplace. Other acts of violence perpetrated by Jayhawkers and militiamen against southern sympathizers turned the James boy into outlaws. They formed a band including the Younger brothers, among others, and resolved to seize the living denied them by attacking the most unpopular institution of the day—the bank. No one was more hated in the border country than the banker, with his exorbitant interest rates and his unsympathetic ear to the plight of townsman and farmer.

The James boys were both feared and idolized. Border staters, mostly according to their political convictions, saw them either as avengers of injustice or as cold-blooded killers who cloaked their criminal acts with a pretense of knight errantry.

Already a host of stories, whose truth or falsehood could not be accurately determined, had grown up around Jesse. After the robbery of the Corydon, Iowa, bank in 1873, the gang—as was its usual custom—split up and went their several ways. Jesse rode off alone, and after a few hours two possemen caught up with him. By then the bandit had put on farmer's clothes. Without giving the possemen a chance to question him, he successfully talked them into searching for two men he claimed had stolen his horses. Finally he managed to slip away.

Once, after a train robbery, the gang was forced to take refuge in a large cave. So fierce was the reputation of the James gang that lawmen preferred to camp outside the cave, rather than go in after the bandits. When a week's vigil failed to starve the gang out, possemen moved cautiously into the cave. They found only the five horses—Jesse and his men had made their escape by means of an underground stream.

Before leaving the site of another train robbery, Jesse had handed the conductor an envelope and asked him to give it to the editor of the local newspaper. The envelope, he added, contained an exact account of the holdup, and he preferred this to be published rather than the exaggerated account that would otherwise have appeared.

There were many tales of Jesse's marksmanship, but perhaps the most famous James story was that of Jesse and the widow. Shortly after the war's end, he and a companion who had been in Quantrell's command were riding through a mountain district of Tennessee. They stopped at the house of a widow whose husband, a guerrilla with Quantrell, had died a short time before of wounds received during the last of the hostilities. Jesse had fought in the same company with her husband in the war.

The widow was in very sad straits. Her house and farm were mortgaged for five hundred dollars, and payment was due that day. In a few hours, she told them, the sheriff and the moneylender were coming to foreclose the mortgage and order her off the place. Jesse had five hundred dollars with him. He gave the widow the money, instructing her to get a correct receipt.

The two men said good-by and rode away, but they didn't go very far. A short distance from the house they dismounted and led their horses into the brush. An hour later two men in a buggy drove by in the direction of the widow's homestead. Jesse and his companion waited, and when the two came driving back along the road, they jumped out, halted the buggy and ordered the occupants to identify themselves.

As expected, they were the sheriff and the moneylender. Jesse relieved the latter of his five hundred dollars and told them to drive on. Then he took the money back to the widow.

Jesse James was known as a man who stole from the rich to give to the poor, but public indignation over the depredations of the James gang led to the posting of rewards by the governors of Missouri and Arkansas for its capture. It also resulted in the hiring of the Pinkerton Detective Agency. After the Gad's Hill robbery in January, 1874, Pinkerton operative Louis Lull joined a posse pursuing the gang through the Ozarks.

Accompanied by a deputy sheriff, Lull stopped at the house of a farmer named Snuffer, known to be related to one of the Younger brothers. When Snuffer answered the door, Lull asked directions to the next town. Jim and John Younger, hiding in the kitchen, decided they didn't like the strangers' looks. Leaving the house, they took a shortcut and waited for Lull and the deputy to turn a bend in the road. Their first volley wounded Lull, but he was able to pull his revolver and fire. John Younger slumped over, dead. Crazed with grief, Jim Younger killed the deputy and pumped two more bullets into Lull before riding off. Lull died six weeks later. When questioned, Snuffer admitted the Younger brothers had been his guests.

"That's about it," Whicher said, reaching for a glass of water. "Have I done my homework?"

Allan Pinkerton nodded. "You get full marks. But I want to tell you this, John. Yours is a very dangerous assignment —the James boys, far from being hounded by their neighbors, have the support of many people in Clay County. A regular intelligence system keeps them informed of any strangers or suspicious persons. I want you to watch your step."

Whicher got to his feet. "Don't worry, Chief. I might not come back with Jesse James, but I mean to come back alive."

The Pinkertons heard from their operative a week later. He wired them from Liberty, Missouri: "Have contacted Mr. Adkins, a local banker. Adkins discouraged me from trying to arrest the James brothers, but finally agreed to introduce me to Colonel Moss, an ex-county sheriff who has much information on them."

Colonel Moss, it developed, was as pessimistic as the banker. As Whicher reported to the Chief, Moss characterized any attempt to capture the James boys using less than twenty men as foolhardy, and predicted the bandit would know Whicher was coming before he was within ten miles of the Kearny homestead.

"This Moss is right," the Chief told Bill Pinkerton. "Wire John to come back."

Bill glanced at the calendar. "It's too late, Dad. He's already left Liberty for the James place."

Three days later a Liberty farmer found the body of a man lying in a ditch. He had been shot five times.

Not having heard from John Whicher, Allan and Bill Pinkerton arrived in Liberty to ask questions. They heard of an unidentified body at the county morgue, and went there to view it—it was John's.

Bill said with a catch in his throat, "The only thing we have to be grateful for is that he didn't have a family."

Allan Pinkerton was filled with grief and rage. "Two of our best men dead, within a month! We've got to even the score, Bill. We've got to get the James boys."

Bill tried to fight a mounting sense of futility. "But how? It's as if we're besieging a fortress in hostile country with a handful of men. The James gang have this county in their pocket. They were waiting for John. They must have known his every movement."

"We'll arrest them yet," his father said grimly. "There's no peace for me until we do."

Another detective, Jack Ladd, volunteered to act as intelligence agent in James country, sending back information on the James brothers' movements. He got a job as farmhand on the Askew place, a few miles from the Samuels homestead in Kearny, and soon had a nodding acquaintance with Frank and Jesse.

It took eight months, until January, 1875, before Ladd was able to wire the Chief with assurance that the James boys would be at the Samuels place for a period of two weeks, long enough to plan and launch an attack. Father and son immediately left for Kansas City, where they set up secret headquarters at a hotel. Meanwhile Ladd kept watch on the Samuels place with the help of several Clay County men and a number of Pinkerton operatives.

On January 5 Allan Pinkerton received a message in code that Frank and Jesse had been seen at the Samuels farm.

Bill Pinkerton left Kansas City for Kearny to act as general in the attack.

At midnight on a cold, moonlit night the posse surrounded the Samuels house. The homestead was dark; evidently Jesse and Frank had sensed some kind of danger.

William Pinkerton had given orders that no shots were to be fired and no hostile actions taken until he gave the command. One of the Pinkerton men, however, lost his head. Forcing open a window on the side of the house, he tossed a flare lamp into the parlor. Dr. Samuels poked the lamp into the fireplace, where a bright fire was roaring. The lamp exploded, mortally wounding Archie Samuels, Jesse's younger half-brother, and tearing off Mrs. Samuels' arm. Dr. Samuels was slightly wounded, as was a Negro servant.

When the Pinkerton and Clay County men rushed into the house, they found only the innocent, the wounded, and the dying.

A few hours later a wrathful Allan Pinkerton tongue-lashed the operative who had brought blood on the Pinkerton name, and summarily dismissed him from the agency's employ. The newspapers made no mention of this when they denounced Allan and William Pinkerton for a "dastardly deed, conceived in cowardice and executed in gore." Nor did they mention the two Pinkerton men who had died under Jesse James' guns, or the others the bandits had murdered in the course of their raids and robberies.

A Kansas City reporter received a letter in which the bandit swore to kill Allan Pinkerton for the "bombing" of his family. Bill told his father he needed a bodyguard.

The Chief laughed. "Son, Jesse might come to Chicago, and he might get me in his sights, but he's never going to pull the trigger. Why? Because he'll want me to know it's Jesse James who's pulling it, and I've never seen the fellow, or a picture of him, in my life."

This prediction proved uncannily correct. Years later a friend of Jesse's told a reporter that Jesse James had spent four months in Chicago on the trail of Allan Pinkerton. More than once he had had him in his sights but, in line with his code, had never squeezed the trigger. The bandit insisted upon giving the detective a chance in a fair fight, and since the two men never met face to face, the opportunity never presented itself.

The price the Samuels family had paid was a bitter one, but the "bombing" of the house in Kearny resulted in a change of public attitude toward the James gang. Many men of prominence went on record with the opinion that if the James brothers and other ex-guerrillas were to be officially pardoned for their wartime activities, they would never trouble law and order again.

A bill was introduced into the Missouri House of Representatives offering amnesty to Jesse, Frank and their associates for crimes committed during the war, provided they were willing to stand trial for the crimes they had been charged with after Appomattox. The bill failed to pass.

In April, 1875, Daniel Askew, who had hired Jack Ladd and whom Jesse believed to be in Pinkerton pay, was shot and killed while drawing water from his well.

There was no proof the James boys had committed the murder, but once again public sentiment reversed itself and swung back against the bandits. Bill Pinkerton thought that now was the time to send another posse into Missouri to bring the James boys back, dead or alive.

Allan Pinkerton was against it. "Sentiment for and against the Jameses has been too fickle to suit me. I won't risk another man until we're sure the people of Clay County are solidly behind us."

"You mean to wait until the gang commits another major crime?" asked Bill.

"We have no choice," the Chief said regretfully.

The major crime Bill spoke of was committed eight months later. A train was stopped at Muncie, outside of Kansas City, and forty thousand dollars in gold taken. After dividing the loot, Jesse and Frank headed back to Clay County, and the Younger brothers to Texas. Allan Pinkerton had no knowledge of this, but he reasoned from past experience that the Youngers, after making a haul, were likely to return to their favorite Texas haunts. He sent an operative to Dallas.

Three months later this operative wired back to Chicago that he had located the Youngers in Dallas. There they had become pillars of the community. The brothers sang in the choir of the Baptist Church and "were of great help" in aiding the local marshal to round up and arrest "criminal characters." "Perhaps the Youngers have reformed," the operative concluded.

"I doubt it," was Allan Pinkerton's dry comment.

While the Youngers were being hunted down in Texas, Bill Pinkerton had been busy organizing an improved intelligence system in Clay County. Among its members were trainmen, farmhands, traveling peddlers, law officers and ordinary citizens. Some knew the James brothers on sight; others, who did not, had instructions to wire the Pinkerton office in Kansas City anytime they saw a medium-sized horseman, handsome and soberly dressed, who had a nervous habit of blinking his eyes, "especially when angry."

Jesse was seen in places as far apart as Los Angeles and Cincinnati, and sometimes on the same day. He was never captured, let alone identified in follow-up investigations.

Early in May, 1875, the San Antonio stage was held up by five masked men near Austin, Texas. Three thousand dollars in valuables and cash were taken from the passengers. The Pinkerton man in Dallas was successful in trailing the gang to one of its several hideouts. Bill Pinkerton came from Kansas City to launch a raid. But again Jesse James' sixth sense of danger saved him. When axes broke in the door, the outlaw had been on the road toward home for several hours.

In July of the next year a train was held up at Rocky Cut, near Otterville, Missouri. The express car was rifled of eighteen thousand dollars. After the loot had been tied across one of the horses, the leader of the masked raiders turned and shouted to the express agent: "If you boys see any of the Pinkertons, tell 'em we're ready for 'em to come and get us!" He laughed, then wheeled his horse into the dark.

Two months later there occurred the most elaborate robbery ever planned by Jesse James. An eight-man gang thundered into Northfield, Minnesota, and attacked the First National Bank. It proved a disaster for the James bunch. Local citizens fought back with rifle and shotgun, and although two of them died from gunshot wounds, two of the bandits were killed. The survivors, Jesse in the lead, galloped out of Northfield in a rain of lead.

After five days of aimless wandering through swampy country, the gang separated near the town of Mankato. Frank and Jesse headed south toward home. Cole, Bob and Jim Younger, along with a gunman named Charlie Pitts, went southwest toward the town of Medalia.

By this time local sheriffs, Pinkerton men and vigilantes had been organized into a huge army. Both bandit groups had a series of close shaves, but managed to escape. After reaching the town of Shieldville, the James brothers were safe. But the band led by Cole Younger was less fortunate.

Two weeks after the robbery, one of the Pinkertons trailing the fugitives wired Allan Pinkerton in Chicago that part of the James gang had been cornered in Matawan County, Minnesota. The Chief and Bill Pinkerton rushed there on the next train. But they were too late. In a gun battle near

Medalia, Charlie Pitts was killed and the three Youngers badly wounded. They were taken under heavy guard to the Flanders Hotel, which served the town as both jail and hospital.

Allan Pinkerton interviewed Cole Younger, a big man with red whiskers. Younger readily admitted his identity to the detective chief, and seemed flattered to be talking to so famous a man. But he flatly refused to admit Frank and Jesse had taken part in the attempted Northfield robbery, let alone discuss their route of escape.

"Cole, you know the jig's up, don't you?" said the detective. "You've had too much bad luck lately. If you talk, I'll see what I can do with the authorities."

The outlaw grinned, despite his painful face wound. "Can't talk, Mr. P. If I did, Jesse James would shut my mouth for me, permanent."

"Not afraid of a mere man, are you?"

Younger grinned again. "Let's just say Jesse can draw a tenth of a second faster than I can."

The Younger brothers stood trial when they were well enough to appear before a court. Each was sentenced to life at state prison.

For a year there was silence from Clay County. As Allan Pinkerton found out later, the outlaw during this time lived with his family in Tennessee, California and Missouri under an assumed name. In Nashville Jesse was bold enough to enter a horse in a state fair, ride it himself and win first prize. A local sheriff watched him accept it without recognizing the handsome, dapper jockey.

Then rumors reached Kansas City that Jesse James was back in Missouri, and had formed a new gang.

In October, 1879, a train was flagged down near Glendale, Missouri. Five masked bandits leaped aboard. The express agent was brutally beaten when he tried to hide the money, and the bandits made off with more than thirty-five thousand dollars.

Bill Pinkerton set off again on the outlaw trail, covering hundreds of miles on horseback in an attempt to question witnesses, most of whom were unwilling to give information. About all Bill learned was the identity of the new gang members.

In December, Marshal Liggett of Kansas City made a sensational announcement: Jesse James was dead. A man named George Shepherd had killed him. Liggett went on to say that he had hired Shepherd, an ex-convict who had once known Jesse James, for the job. Armed with a specially prepared news clipping which told that he was the object of an extensive police hunt, Shepherd had found the gang near Granby, Missouri, and killed Jesse James in an exchange of revolver shots. Shepherd himself had escaped.

"Let me see Jesse James dead," Allan Pinkerton replied when reporters asked him to comment. Not for one moment did he believe the story, and in March, 1881, Jesse and Frank led their gang in the robbery of a stagecoach near Muscle Shoals, Alabama. Again, in July, they robbed the bank in Riverton, Iowa, of six thousand dollars.

Bill Pinkerton was in Iowa two days later. But the James boys had too good a head start. His father consoled him when Bill returned to Kansas City. "It won't be long now. Jesse's tired and must want to quit for good. But not before he's gathered a lot more loot in a last series of raids."

Now the Pinkertons applied pressure. Operatives covered areas in four states, haunting Jesse's friends and the farmhouse in Kearny, investigating houses in lonely places that might offer the outlaws shelter. Still others traveled trains and express cars likely to be the next object of the bandits' attention.

A short time after the Riverton robbery, masked bandits

held up a train near Winston, Missouri. When the shooting was over, two men lay dead from Jesse James' Navy Colts. The robbery yielded only six hundred dollars.

Governor Thomas Crittenden of Missouri, sworn to destroy the James gang, offered a ten-thousand-dollar reward for the conviction and capture of Frank and Jesse James. Missouri railroads supplied the funds.

In September the gang struck for a second time at Blue Cut, near Glendale, robbing train passengers of close to two thousand dollars. With a rather forced bravado, Jesse James formally introduced the members of his gang to the engineer and express clerk: "Meet Frank James, Wood Hite, Clarence Hite, Dick Liddell, Ed Miller and Charlie Ford. I expect you to remember our names for the newspapers."

The gang abruptly disappeared into hiding. Pinkertons were everywhere, and the relentless pressure had begun to tell. Now gang members were openly afraid of Jesse, uncertain what he might do next. Gang morale crumbled. Disgusted, Jesse turned back to Missouri with one of his men, Ed Miller. On the way they got into an argument and Jesse killed Miller.

The rest of the gang left for home. Wood Hite and Dick Liddell stopped off at the Ford farmhouse in Ray County. Nerves were tense. The next day Dick Liddell killed Hite in an argument over whether Liddell had stolen a hundred dollars from the receipts of the Blue Cut robbery.

Shortly after Hite's death Jesse arrived at the Ford farmhouse, accompanied by Charlie Ford. Mistrustful of the man who had killed Ed Miller, Liddell left for other parts. "Jesse's gun is too quick these days," he commented to Bob Ford, Charlie's brother.

Bob Ford had his own plans for Jesse. He had already met with Governor Crittenden to talk over the reward. On the morning of April 3, 1882, he shot and killed the outlaw king while Jesse stepped to the wall to straighten a picture.

Allan and Bill Pinkerton heard the news at their Kansas City headquarters. The same morning Jesse James died from a bullet in the back of his head, the detective chief received a wire from a Pinkerton in Ray County who said he hoped to have definite word of James' whereabouts within the next twelve hours!

Jesse James was dead, but there was no rejoicing at the Pinkerton office. Not because Pinkerton men had failed to bring him in, but because the long hunt was over, the chase done. And life, a detective's life, would never be quite the same again.

"Well, it's finished," Allan Pinkerton said. "And I didn't get Jesse."

Bill looked at his father sadly. Jesse James had been Allan Pinkerton's last case. Allan was sixty-three now and due to retire later in the year, after which Bill and his brother would take over management of agency affairs.

"Look at it this way, Dad," Bill said in an effort to cheer him. "You didn't get Jesse, no. But neither did he get you."

The Chief laughed. "I guess you're right, Bill. I'll have to settle for that."

Frank James gave himself up to Governor Crittenden five months later, in Jefferson City, Missouri. He was tried for the murder of a stonemason during a holdup in 1881, and found not guilty. He slipped into obscurity quickly. The James story was over, but not its legend, made of more imperishable stuff.

13 The King is Dead

BEGINNING IN 1877, THE CHIEF HAD EMBARKED ON A PART-time literary career, the writing of autobiographical stories and anecdotes of his own adventures and those of his more colorful agents. After the agency had become famous, a rash of dime novels featuring a Pinkerton-like detective named "Old Sleuth" had appeared and sold in the tens of thousands. Allan Pinkerton saw no reason why the genuine article might not do as well, or better. His first effort, *The Gypsies and the Detectives*, published by Carleton & Co. in 1873, had gone into several editions. His publishers were so pleased that they asked the Chicago author for the right to bring out all his future books.

In the next several years Carleton & Co. and other book houses issued eighteen volumes of the Pinkerton reminiscences on an average of more than two a year. Almost all achieved the status of best-sellers. Some of the more outstanding titles were: *The Spy of the Rebellion, The Bankrobbers and the Detectives, the Railroad Forger and the Detectives, The Expressman and the Detectives, the Molly Maguires and the Detectives, The Professional Thieves and the Detectives, Criminal Reminiscences,* and *Thirty Years a Detective.*

Most of these titles were under three hundred pages long, others ran to six and even seven hundred. They were written after office hours and on the road during his visits to various branches of the agency. As he was fond of pointing out to his readers in preface after preface, these "criminal memoirs" had been published not only to amuse a public with the excitement and romance of a good detective story, but to demonstrate "the enduring morality of strict integrity and honorable conduct."

He was careful to change the names of the criminals who figured so prominently in his narratives, so that no extra obstacles to reformation should stand in their way.

The Chief had always planned to make use of the voluminous records of people, places and things he had begun collecting as early as 1850 when the agency began. However, in the Chicago fire of 1871 all these personal records were destroyed.

"I'll never write a book now," he told Joan despairingly.

She gave him a reproving look. "Don't say that, Allan. When a man has a mind like yours, he doesn't need complete records."

It wasn't until 1882, when his file cabinets had filled up again, that the Chief launched his full scale literary career. It took so much of his time that Joan was relieved when he retired and turned agency affairs over to Bill and Robert. Her industrious husband might work as hard at his writing as he had at pursuing criminals, but at least he was home all day, and at regular intervals she could coax him out of his study for a cup of tea or a chat.

To her surprise, Joan found herself listening to Allan's narratives, adding a word or phrase here, a correction there. Soon she was correcting proofs and sometimes rewriting entire chapters—Allan had a tendency to run on. Her husband couldn't deny that Joan's blue pencil improved his books considerably.

"You deserve to be listed as co-author," he told her, "and I'm writing Carleton in New York to that effect."

Joan threw up her hands in horror. Despite her interest in his writing, she felt, like many women of her time, that writing books had something immoral about it. "Allan Pinkerton," she said, "you'll do no such thing! Why the ladies would cut me dead in the street!"

A literary career, then as now, had its hazards. In 1883, after the Chief had published his best book, *The Spy of the Rebellion,* he received a great number of letters. Most were favorable, but one man from Ohio took exception to the author's unflattering portrait of Abraham Lincoln as a military man. He not only wrote several angry letters but, one morning, appeared at the Chief's Chicago home in person.

"Mr. Pinkerton," he said coldly, "we must have a talk. I feel you have maligned President Lincoln in stating McClellan's case so strongly."

Allan Pinkerton knew a fanatic when he saw one. "I'm sorry, sir," he told him, "but I'm very busy," and shut the front door in his face.

Fanatics aren't gotten rid of all that easily. A few minutes later the servant girl entered the Chief's study. "Sir," she said, "that gentleman's at the back door now. He says he won't go away until you talk to him."

The Chief groaned. "Put your coat on, Liza, and get Patrolman McGinnis. He's probably down the street somewhere."

While Liza was looking for the policeman, the fanatic returned to the front of the house. A knot of curious bystanders gathered around him and listened with great interest as he shouted: "Abe was right! Little Mac was a good general when he wasn't retreating, but Lincoln did right to fire him! Can you deny that, Pinkerton?" The man had covered the Peninsular Campaign, and was halfway through the battle of Antietam when Patrolman McGinnis arrived and took him to the station house.

The couple spent much of their time at their country estate, Larch Farm, in Onarga, which had become one of the showplaces of northern Illinois. There was an artificial lake, a swimming pool and beautiful drives and grounds planted with thousands of larch trees imported from Scotland. Hard-surfaced roads led to the 250-acre farm's three gates, and another roadway ran to a special railway siding where private cars of the great and famous could be parked. The main building, a replica of a gentleman's mansion Allan Pinkerton had once seen as a boy in Scotland, was one-and-a-half stories high, with a windowed cupola on its roof. A wine cellar and root house were built near the main building, along with an unusual structure called the "Snuggery." This long, low building had an oval roof which was covered with canvas on the inside. A Scots painter spent nearly two years painting heroic, kilted Scots on its walls.

The Chief was a man who spoke his mind, and he made some enemies in Onarga. These people, who had heard garbled versions of the sanctuary Allan Pinkerton had provided Jimmy McParland after the Molly Maguire trials, spread rumors that he hid escaped criminals in the "Snuggery." The Chief laughed when he heard these stories. "From detective to criminal in thirty years!" he was fond of joking when a friend repeated some variation of the malicious rumors.

Besides using Larch Farm as a country place where he could entertain distinguished visitors, the Chief also used it as a haven for the recreation and recuperation of his operatives. No care or expense was spared to guarantee their privacy, and guards were stationed at all gates to keep out curiosity-seekers. There was one strict rule: visitors who drove their horses along the drive at a pace faster than a walk were fined five dollars for raising dust that settled on the flowers.

One such visitor was an Illinois senator famous for his sharp tongue. The senator had enjoyed Allan Pinkerton's port and cigars, but his carriage nonetheless raised dust on the flower beds, and the guards stopped it at the gate.

"What's the meaning of this?" the senator demanded when his host arrived at the gatehouse.

"Senator, you exceeded the speed limit and must pay a five-dollar fine," the Chief told him.

"Pinkerton, you're mad!" bellowed the senator. "Mad, or a pauper. If you're that broke, I'll be glad to help you out." Contemptuously he handed him a ten-dollar bill.

The Chief ignored the money. "Give the senator five dollars change, John," he told the guard and, turning on his heel, marched back to the house.

In 1882 the retired Chief and his wife took a trip to Glasgow. Their reception was a warm one. Glasgow made it clear that it considered Allan Pinkerton one of its most illustrious sons. The mayor gave him a testimonial dinner, attended by city notables, and when the Chief took a walk in Queen's Park, a respectful crowd followed him along the paths. Before leaving the park he delivered an impromptu talk on the opportunities to be found in America.

Of the Pinkerton family in Glasgow only brother Robert was still alive. The brothers reminisced about old times over tea and scones and paid a visit to the Gorbels. The onetime slum district was unrecognizable. Since the young Chartist had fled Scotland, progress had come to the working class through better pay and a higher standard of living. In place of the squalid flats were pleasant apartment buildings where decently dressed workmen lived in comfort with their well-fed families.

Rob caught his brother's eye. "Seeing this, Allan, do you wonder that you were once a revolutionary?"

The Chief smiled. "No, Rob. If there's one thing I've learned, it's that a man has to fight for what he deserves. He's not going to get it by just wishing or waiting."

In later years, the few years still left to them as man and wife, Joan was to be glad for the Glasgow trip, which had given Allan a new lease on life. In the summer of 1884, while he was working on the galley proofs of *Thirty Years a Detective,* another stroke felled the sixty-five-year-old Chief. He died, without recovering consciousness, on July 1. Joan followed two years later.

The Pinkerton estate was worth over half a million dollars. A lot of money, but in the light of the opportunities Allan Pinkerton had to become a multimillionaire, it tends to shrink to something less than a "fortune." In the era of the Robber Barons, Jay Gould, Jim Fisk and many other unscrupulous men, Allan Pinkerton, had he been willing to forget his principles, could have picked up millions of tarnished dollars. That he did not is more proof, if proof were needed, of his stubborn Scots integrity.

William and Robert Pinkerton were both fine detectives and able administrators. Under their direction new branches were opened in Boston, Denver, St. Paul and Kansas City. The brothers changed their father's policy of steering clear of strikes and labor troubles, and firmly allied the agency on the side of management in its mounting conflict with labor unions. Around 1891 Pinkerton's National Detective Agency came under much criticism as the shock troops of ruthless, exploitative capitalism. To many a militant workingman the word "Pinkerton" became a synonym for strikebreaker.

By then Allan Pinkerton had lain in Graceland Cemetery in Chicago for almost nine years. But the reputation of

Pinkerton's Agency in the 1890's was a sadly ironic commentary on the liberal principles of its founder.

Today, long-since purged of its antilabor bias, Pinkerton's is recognized as the world's largest private agency providing investigative and security services for American business and industry. The organization that began in 1850 with a force of nine men has grown into a corporation of more than thirteen thousand employees, with offices in forty-eight cities in the United States and Canada. Pinkerton guards are on duty throughout the United States and Canada in industrial plants, retail establishments, banks, hotels, hospitals, universities and museums. They are also found at all kinds of conventions and athletic events. They service state and local fairs, major race tracks and many other events. Pinkerton's was awarded the sole contract for overall security of the New York World's Fair in 1964–1965. Its current profits total over thirty million dollars a year.

The founder of Pinkerton's National Detective Agency is rightfully deserving of the title, America's First Great Detective. At a time when there was no fingerprinting system for criminals, no federal rogue's gallery or state alarm system, he was a master investigator whose intelligence, organizational abilities, intuition and judgment of men became, fittingly, legendary. Very few major crimes occurred in the United States in the years 1850–1885 in whose detection and solution the Pinkerton Agency had no hand. It is a tribute to Allan Pinkerton's greatness that only two major criminals— Shinburn and James—escaped his net. Though relentless in the tracking down of lawbreakers, he was as generous to those who came to him for help; thousands of Pinkerton dollars went to aid men he captured to go straight. He was more effective as detective than as espionage agent, but his contributions to the first U. S. Secret Service he founded, while perhaps less valuable than Lafayette Baker's, earned the gratitude of such men as Abraham Lincoln, Edwin Stanton and George McClellan. And it is probable that had Allan Pinkerton remained a cooper in Dundee, President Lincoln would not have survived assassins' bullets to take office in 1861.

The Chief's achievement was a great one, but much more important to him than success and fame was something that has nothing whatever to do with either of them: justice. Early in his career he wrote: "The criminal must pay his debt to society, but must not be hunted and persecuted after he has done so. Justice and human decency demand that we help him to become an honest and reputable citizen."

All modern penology is built on these words. They serve well as Allan Pinkerton's epitaph.

Bibliography

Breihan, Carl W. *The Complete and Authentic Life of Jesse James.* New York: Frederick Fell, Inc., 1953.

Horan, James D. *Desperate Men.* New York: Doubleday & Company, Inc., 1962.

―――― and Swiggett, Howard. *The Pinkerton Story.* New York: G. P. Putnam's Sons, 1951.

Hynd, Alan. *The Pinkerton Case Book.* New York: New American Library, 1948.

James, Jesse, Jr. *Jesse James My Father.* New York: Frederick Fell, Inc., 1957.

Lavine, Sigmund A. *Allan Pinkerton, America's First Private Eye.* New York: Dodd, Mead & Co., 1963.

Pinkerton, Allan. *The Bankers, Their Vaults, and the Burglars.* Chicago: Fergus Printing Co., 1873.

――――. *The Bankrobbers and the Detectives.* New York: Carleton & Co., 1883.

――――. *Criminal Reminiscences and Detective Sketches.* New York: Carleton & Co., 1879.

――――. *The Detective and the Somnambulist.* Chicago: Keen, Cooke & Co., 1875.

――――. *The Expressman and the Detectives.* Chicago: Keen, Cooke & Co., 1875.

――――. *The Molly Maguires and the Detectives.* New York: Carleton & Co., 1877.

――――. *The Railroad Forger and the Detectives.* New York: Carleton & Co., 1881.

――――. *The Spy of the Rebellion.* New York: Carleton & Co., 1883.

――――. *Thirty Years a Detective.* New York: Dillingham, 1886.

Rowan, Wilmer R. *The Pinkertons: A Detective Dynasty.* Boston: Little, Brown & Co., 1931.

Index

Abolitionism/Abolitionists, 32, 42-43, 57-58, 59, 64-65, 66, 163
Adams Express Company, 114, 115, 121-22
agents, female, 67, 75, 76, 80, 107-08
Allen, E. J., 85-89, 92, 96-99, 107, 109, 112-14
American Telegraph Company, 72, 73
Ancient Order of Hibernians, 138, 141
Antietam, Battle of, 112
Appomattox County, Virginia, 115
Arkansas, 166
Askew, Daniel, 168, 170
Atwater, Captain, 107-08

Baker, Emily, 107-08
Baker, Lafayette, 113
Baltimore, Maryland, 66-69, 72-73, 75-76, 77-78, 79, 99-101, 102
Bangs, George, 85, 116, 123
Barry, Dick, 124
Beauregard, General, 96
Belgium, 155, 156, 159-60
Benjamin, Judah, 106-07
Bertillon system of identification, 115
Boehm, Carl, 88
books, written by Allan Pinkerton, 177-79
Boston, Massachusetts, 151-52, 182
Bosworth, Increase, 35, 38-39, 40-42
Bowling Green, Kentucky, 85, 89

Braddock, Mr., 153
Bridgeman, Ian, 92
British Isles, 14, 18
Brooklyn, New York, 134, 135
Brown, John, 58, 64-65
Buchanan, James, 79
Buffalo and Erie Railroad, 159
Buffalo, New York, 130
Bull Run, Battle of, 96
Burns, Douglas, 24
Burnside, General Ambrose E., 112

Camp Douglas, 113
Camp Rector, 90-91
Canada, 24, 30, 57, 123-24, 183
Canter, Jack, 134-37
Carfrae, Joan, 21-23. See also Pinkerton, Joan
Carter, Jackson, 58, 63
Central Fire Insurance Company of Philadelphia, 134
Charlestown, Virginia, 65
Chartists, 13-16, 17, 18-20, 22, 23, 24, 32
Chase, Salmon P., 81
Chattanooga, Tennessee, 91
Cherry Hill, Pennsylvania, 137
Chicago, Illinois, 31, 33, 39-40, 43, 44-45, 48, 51, 54, 55, 57, 66, 79, 88, 93, 113, 114, 125, 128, 129, 157-58, 170
Chicago Tribune, The, 132
Church, William, 43

187

Cincinnati, Ohio, 85, 88-89, 123, 158
City National Bank, 152
Civil War, the, 79-113, 115, 116, 163-
  64
Clarkesville, 85
Clay County, Missouri, 163, 164, 167,
  168, 171
Cleveland, Ohio, 125
Coal and Iron Police, 146-47
Colorado, 150
Columbia, Tennessee, 58, 61
Columbia County, Pennsylvania, 146
Columbus, Ohio, 80, 83
Committee of Public Safety, 89-90
Concord, New Hampshire, 153
Connecticut, 152
Cook County, 43
Corydon, Iowa, 165
Council Bluffs, Iowa, 119-21
Craig, John, 36-40
Crane, Henry, 35-36, 38, 39, 40, 42
Crittenden, Governor Thomas, 175,
  176
Curtin, Governor, 74

Dallas, Texas, 171
Davies, Harry, 67-69, 78
Daviess County, Missouri, 118
Delaware, 66
Denver, Colorado, 150, 160, 182
Department of the Ohio, 84
Detroit, Michigan, 30-31, 124-25
Dormer, Mr., 141
Downington, Pennsylvania, 74
Dumfries, Virginia, 106
Dundee, Illinois, 31-33, 35-36, 42, 43,
  46
Durkin, Mr., 141

Eastern Penitentiary, 137
Ellis, Captain, 97-98
England, 14
extradition treaties, 157

Falls City Tobacco Bank, 158
Felton, Samuel, 66, 70, 72, 73
Fergus, Robert, 31
Ferndale, Pennsylvania, 143
Flanders, George, 122

Floyd County, Indiana, 125-26
Ford, Bob, 175
Ford, Charlie, 175
Ford's Theater, 113
Fort Harris, 90
Fort McHenry, 98, 101, 105
Fort Sumter, 79
Fox River, 31, 33
Franciscus, G. C., 72
Franklin, Benjamin, 140-41, 145, 146,
  147
Fredericksburg, Virginia, 107

Gallatin, Missouri, 116, 119
"General Principles" of Pinkerton's
  National, 49-50
Girardville, Pennsylvania, 143
Glasgow, Scotland, 13-24, 181
Glenwood, Iowa, 120
Gowen, Franklin B., 139-40
Grant, Ulysses S., 115, 141
Greenhow, Rose, 95-98
Gurley, Dr., 106

Halifax, 24, 26, 28
Harley, Edgar, 159
Harper's Ferry, Virginia, 64
Harmond, John, 55-57
Harrisburg, Pennsylvania, 72-74
Harrison's Landing, 111
Havre de Grace, Maryland, 66
Hibernian House, 142, 147
Hite, Clarence, 175
Hite, Wood, 175
Hodges, Captain, 26-27
Humboldt, Tennessee, 91-92
Hunt, Joseph, 35, 38-39, 40-42
Huntsville, Alabama, 59
Hutchinson, J. H., 70, 73

Illinois, 35, 39, 42-43, 84, 116, 157
Illinois Central Railroad, 66
Illinois Penitentiary, 57, 157
Independence Hall, 72
Indiana, 84, 93, 116-17, 119, 125-26
Indianapolis, Indiana, 122, 123
Ingham, John, 131-32
Ireland, 138

Jackson, Mississippi, 88, 91
Jackson County, Indiana, 116-17, 123
James, Frank, 162-65, 167-76
James, Jesse, 162-76
James River, 107
James, Robert, 163
Jayhawkers, 163-64
Jefferson, Missouri and Indianapolis Railroad, 122
Johnson, Andrew, 68
Johnson, Ralph, 53-54
Jones, Gomer, 144-46
Judd, Norman, 67, 68, 70, 72-73, 74

Kane, George P., 66, 68-69, 78
Kane County, 32, 35, 42, 43
Kansas, 163-64
Kansas City, Missouri, 168-69, 171, 173, 182
Kearny, Missouri, 163, 164, 167, 168-69
Kehoe, Jack, 142, 144-50
Kentucky, 85, 163
Knights of Liberty, 99-101

Ladd, Jack, 168
Lake Michigan, 51, 55, 57
Larch Farm, 180-81
Lawler, Muff, 141-44
Leary, Mr., 148-49
Lee, Robert E., 64, 112, 115
Lehigh Coal and Navigation Company, 153
Leonardstown, Virginia, 106
Lewis, Price, 92, 109-11
Liberty, Missouri, 167
Liddell, Dick, 175
Liggett, Marshal, 174
Lillie safe, 151
Lincoln, Abraham, 66-77, 79-81, 93, 95, 111, 112-14, 184
Linden, Robert, 147
Littleton, Jock, 59-61
Littleton, Mary, 59-61
Louisiana, 85, 88
Louisville, Kentucky, 85, 125, 158
Lowrey, Mr., 58-60, 61, 64
Lull, Louis, 166-67

McCallum, Captain, 110
McCauley, William, 17-18, 23
McClellan, General George B., 80, 81, 83-85, 92-94, 108, 111, 112-13
McClintoch, Owen, 25-26, 28, 29-30
McDougall, Ian, 19
McPartland, Jimmy, 140-50
McPhail, Mr., 104
MacAndrew, Mr., 144-46, 148-48, 150
MacDonald, Captain, 13, 19-20
Magnolia, Iowa, 119, 121
Marshfield, Indiana, 121-22
Maryland, 66, 79, 100
Mason-Dixon Line, 57, 116
Meara, Walter, 117-18
Memphis, Tennessee, 85, 86-87, 90
Mexican War, 81
Miller, Ed, 175
Milwaukee, Wisconsin, 35, 41
Minerville, Pennsylvania, 141
Minnesota, 172-73
Mississippi, 85, 88
Missouri, 116, 118, 119, 163-64, 166, 170, 173-76
Molly Maguires, the, 138-50
Moore, John, 122-23
Moran, Joe, 157
Morton, Chase, 110
Moss, Colonel, 167
Murphy, Neil, 16

Nashville, Tennessee, 85-86, 173
Negro slaves, 32, 42-43, 57-58, 59, 86-87
New Albany, Indiana, 125-27
New York City, 79, 128, 135, 151, 156, 160, 161
Nicolay, John, 70-72, 80
Northern Central Railroad, 73, 114
Northfield, Minnesota, 172

Oates, Phil, 117-18
Ocean National Bank, 155-56
O'Grady, Terry, 52-54
Ohio, 84, 158
Onarga, Illinois, 150, 180
Ossining, New York, 134-35

Palmetto Guards, 68-69

panel game, 131
Pattmore, May, 129-33
Pennsylvania, 69-70, 72-75, 79, 138-50
Pennsylvania Railroad, 72
Pennsylvania & Reading Railroad, 134
Pennsylvania State Insurance Commission, 134
Perryman, Maryland, 80
Perryville, 75
Philadelphia, Pennsylvania, 69-72, 73, 80, 134, 139, 143, 146, 149
Philadelphia and Reading Railroad, 139
Philadelphia, Wilmington and Baltimore Railroad, 66-67
Pierce, Mr., 110
Pillow, General Gideon, 87
Pinkerton, Allan, boyhood, 13-19; wants to be a policeman, 16; quits school to work, 16; as apprentice in barrel making, 18; death of father, 19; in Chartist movement, 19-20, 23; marriage, 23; his name on arrest list, 24; on ship to Canada, 25-28; rescues friend, 29; settles in Dundee, Illinois, 31-32; is an Abolitionist, 32, 42-43, 57-58, 59; his children, 32, 46, 47; solves counterfeiting case, 32-33, 35-40; appointed deputy sheriff, 43; as special agent, 44; as Chicago's first detective, 44-45; his own detective agency, 46-47, 48ff.; establishes code of practice, 49-50; French Cemetery case and, 51-54; catches hotel jewel thief, 54-57; adds wigs and disguises, 57; Slocum case and, 58-63; tries to free John Brown, 65; hires women detectives, 67; foils plot to assassinate Lincoln, 68-78; discusses organizing secret service, 80-81; saves Webster from lynching, 82-83; his agency gathers intelligence for McClellan, 85-92; with the Secret Service, 93, 95-113; son Bill joins him, 95; death of Webster, 111-12; son Bob joins Secret Service, 113; solves Adams Express case, 114; sets up criminal file, 115; the Reno gang and, 116-27; assassination attempt on him, 124; Trafton case and, 128-33; Jack Canter and, 134-37; helps rehabilitate criminals, 137; the Molly Maguires and, 139-50; his country home, 150, 180-81; brings mother to U. S., 150; Max Shinburn and, 153-57; suffers paralytic stroke, 156; Walter Sheridan and, 158-61; the James gang and, 162-63, 166-76; retires, 176; as author, 177-79, 182; visits Glasgow, 181; death, 182; his agency to date, 182-83; deserves title America's First Great Detective, 183-84
Pinkerton, Isabella (mother), 13-15, 17, 19-21, 24, 150
Pinkerton, Joan (wife), 23-25, 28-32, 41, 43-44, 45, 46-47, 51, 58, 92-93, 95, 113, 126, 178-79, 182. *See also* Carfrae, Joan
Pinkerton, Joan (daughter), 46, 47, 93, 113, 126
Pinkerton, John (brother), 13-15, 19
Pinkerton, Robert (brother), 13-15, 18, 181-82
Pinkerton, Robert (son), 46, 47, 93, 113, 119, 126-33, 160-61, 176, 182
Pinkerton, Sergeant William (father), 13-16, 18, 19
Pinkerton, William (son), 32, 43, 47, 93, 113, 119-21, 124-25, 126-31, 132-33, 134, 136, 158, 159-60, 162, 167-72, 174, 176, 182
Pinkerton's National Detective Agency, 46-47, 48-84, 114-25, 128-76, 182-83
Pitts, Charlie, 172-73
Pittsburgh, Pennsylvania, 80, 81-83
"private eyes," 114

Quantrell, William Clarke, 163-64

Reno, Clint, 116, 119
Reno, Frank, 116, 119, 120-21, 123-27
Reno, John, 116, 117-19
Reno, Laura, 116

Reno, Simeon, 116, 119, 121, 123, 125-27

Reno, William, 116, 119, 121, 123, 125-27

Rhode Island, 152

Richmond, Virginia, 78, 92, 93, 96, 98, 104, 106, 107, 109-11

Richmond Enquirer, The, 110

Rock Island Railroad, 45

Rocky Cut, Missouri, 172

Rogers, Michael, 120-21

Sable Island, 30

St. Louis, Missouri, 157, 158

St. Paul, Minnesota, 182

Samuels, Archie, 169

Samuels, Mrs., 163, 169

Samuels, Dr. Reuben, 163, 164, 169

Sanford, E. S., 72

Schultz, Wilhelm, 32, 43, 46

Schuylkill County, Pennsylvania, 146

Scobell, John, 105-06

Scotland, 14, 23, 150

Scott, Thomas A., 95, 97-98

Scott, General Winfield, 72, 81, 83, 92, 93

Scranton, Pennsylvania, 143

Scully, John, 109-11

Seward, William H., 72, 123, 124

Seymour, Indiana, 116-19, 123

Shenandoah, Pennsylvania, 141-49

Shepherd, George, 174

Sheridan, Walter, 157-61

Shields, Indiana, 122

Shinburn, Max, 151-57

Sing Sing Prison, 134-35

Sloan, Sam, 105

Slocum, John, 58-63

Smith, George, 35, 41-42

Springfield, Illinois, 67

Stanton, Edwin, 111, 113

Stark, Joseph, 153-54

Susquehanna Ferry, 67

Susquehanna River, 75

Sweeney, Steward, 26-28

Tamaqua, Pennsylvania, 147, 149

Tennessee, 58, 85, 90, 165, 173

Tennessee River, 89

Texas, 171-72

Tracy, John F., 45-46

Trafton, Stanley, 128-29, 133

Tredegar Ironworks, 107-08

Trenton, Pennsylvania, 140-41

Underground Railroad, the, 42-43, 57-58, 59

U. S. Secret Service, 80-81, 93-113

Vermont, 152

Vincent, Henry, 19

Virginia, 92, 93, 105-06

Wales, 14

Walker, Eaton, 36

Warne, Kate, 67, 75, 76, 80

Warner, Francis, 128

Washington, D.C., 66, 68, 72, 77, 79, 80, 93, 95-96, 100, 106, 108, 109, 111

Waverly House Hotel, 55, 56-57

"We Never Sleep," 47

Webster, Timothy, 60-63, 67-68, 75, 78, 80, 82-83, 85, 89-92, 99-107, 109-12

West Philadelphia, Pennsylvania, 74-75

Whicher, John, 162-63, 167-68

White Haven, Pennsylvania, 153

Wilkes-Barre, Pennsylvania, 147, 154-55

Williams, George, 158

Wilson, Mr., 154

Windsor, Canada, 123-24

Winscott, Robert, 117-18

Wisconsin, 35

Yates, B. C., 33-34, 35-36, 38, 40, 43

Younger, Bob, 164, 172-73

Younger, Cole, 164, 172-73

Younger, Jim, 164, 166-67, 172-73

Younger, John, 164, 166-67

Zigler, Bill, 102-03

About the Author

ARTHUR ORRMONT was born in Albany, New York, moved to Brooklyn where he graduated from Erasmus Hall High School. Interested in writing from the age of twelve, he attended the University of Michigan, where he was a three-time winner of the Avery Hopwood award in creative writing. After graduate work at Cornell, he came to New York where he remained for the next twelve years. He resigned as executive editor of a large publishing firm in 1957, and is now doing free-lance writing of short stories, magazine articles and books, both adult and juvenile.